Classic
American
Ghost Stories

Classic American Ghost Stories

200 Years of Ghost Lore from
the Great Plains, New England,
the South and the Pacific Northwest

edited by Deborah L. Downer

August House Publishers, Inc.

LITTLE ROCK

Published by August House, Inc.,
P.O. Box 3223, Little Rock, Arkansas, 72203,
501-372-5450.

Printed in the United States of America

10 9 8 7 6 5 4 3 2

LIBRARY OF CONGRESS CATALOGING-IN-PUBLICATION DATA
Classic American ghost stories: 200 years of ghost lore from the
Great Plains, New England, the South, and the Pacific Northwest
Edited by Deborah L. Downer.–1st ed. p. cm.
ISBN 0-87463-115-6 (alk. paper)
ISBN 0-87463-118-0 (pbk.: alk. paper)
1. Ghosts–United States 2. n-us.
I. Downer, Deborah L., 1954- .
BF 1472.U6C55 1990
133.1'0973–dc20   90–34782
CIP

Cover illustration by Byron Taylor
Typography by Lettergraphics
Design direction by Ted Parkhurst
Project direction by Liz Parkhurst
Editorial assistance by Ed Gray & Judith Faust

This book is printed on archival-quality paper which meets the
guidelines for performance and durability of the Committee on
Production Guidelines for Book Longevity of the Council on
Library Resources.

AUGUST HOUSE, INC.   PUBLISHERS   LITTLE ROCK

*To Ellis and Marian Downer
for their love and support*

*and to Clara Strickland
for her excellent teaching and example*

Contents

Preface

I REMEMBER AS A CHILD BEING afraid of thunderstorms, which were frequent occurences along the Chesapeake tidewater where I spent most summers on a farm in Lancaster County, Virginia. My aunt Allean McNeal would read to me from a battered old book of spooky stories until the storm played itself out and the sky cleared.

The stories fascinated me. After a while, I began to look forward to storms. I'd run for the book every time the sky turned dark.

In 1965 my family moved to Hamlet, North Carolina, where my father bought a white colonial-style house with a wide front porch. He wanted to remodel it. The house had been deserted for nine years, and looked it: broken windows, splintered steps, torn screens, chalky paint, the yard a jungle of grass, weeds, and leaves.

My new friends told me the house was haunted. Ghost stories, whether I like it or not, seem to be a recurring feature of my life.

So when my sister Diane suggested I work on a manuscript, my love of ghost stories and the mysterious evolved into a study of man's unending fascination with the unnatural and the unseen. A special interest for me became the wide range of tales found in our American homeland.

The ghost stories I grew up with were regionally-oriented collections, telling of haunted southern mansions or ghost ships in New England bays, deserted western mines or lost treasures in Cajun bayous, monsters in the Great Lakes or sunken Spanish galleons along the Outer Banks.

There's no denying that ghosts are entities of mass consciousness appearing in every land, culture, and language. The Scottish moors with their foggy meadows are rich ground for tales of werewolves and demons who step out of the dark and snatch up unsuspecting humans. Long-deserted castles in the British Isles are home to tormented dead souls, walking their hallways, moaning their stories of woe. There are ancient African tales of alien creatures falling from the sky, stories of sea monsters in the South Pacific, and legends of abominable snowmen in the mountains of Asia.

America's melting-pot diversity creates perhaps the widest variety of ghostlore in the world. Our ghostlore is inextricably intertwined with our history, and is a rich part of our American heritage.

Why, I asked myself, should we have only anthologies restricted to a specific region, or dialect, or setting, when our country has such a vast and colorful store of ghostlore? It seemed to me an anthology should itself be a melting pot of lore from east, west, north, and south. That's what I set about to compile in this collection.

There is something of universal appeal about ghost stories, strange tales, mystic places, and eerie phenomena. Where does fantasy end? Where does reality begin? Anyone who has walked down a moonlit road at night, and at least once looked nervously over a shoulder to see what might lurk behind, knows about the hair-raising unknown.

My neighbors Rosemary and Wilce Whaley invited me over for dinner one night, and when they learned I was putting this anthology together, Wilce told an eerie tale.

In 1941, Wilce and a friend were coming home one night from a late date, walking down a lonely dirt road. The road was short, and the moon was full. They could see well.

Columbus County, North Carolina, near Nakina, is good farmland, and Wilce described this road as running the length of a field. The field, separated from the road by a two-foot ditch, was on his right; the woods were on his left.

He and his friend walked along chatting about the evening

until Wilce saw what looked like a big, black dog just to his right. The dog crouched in the ditch, then jumped out onto the road just as the young men came alongside. Wilce took a step and kicked at the dog to scare it away. His foot met thin air. The "dog" vanished. Was it a dog? We'll never know. Wilce is certain of two things: the "dog" was there, and then it wasn't. He's never forgotten.

Human beings are confronted with the supernatural from our first childhood encounter with a "boogey man" in the closet, until that final moment when we take a last breath and must face what awaits us on the other side. Experiences like Wilce's, I've found, are more common than most would admit.

Primitive man feared the inexplicable nature of wind, rain, and fire, so he made them gods. Modern man fears the supernatural, so he labels such concepts irrational, figments of worn imaginations.

Even in denial, we retain our awe of the supernatural, relishing our tales of risen spirits, haunted places, and cursed lands. Perhaps it is only natural for us mortals to create illusions around the things that scare us most, so that in confronting our fears, we overcome them.

While intellectuals theorize about ghostlore as a psychological mechanism—a cathartic exhumation of buried fears, a raising of subconscious demons into the light of reason—maybe the best and simplest explanation for our preoccupation with ghostlore is the one my childhood friend Beth McNair offered.

I'm a bigger coward than she, and when we watch scary stories on television I do it with my hand over my eyes while she narrates what's happening on screen. During one especially gruesome telecast, I complained, "What is this fascination people have with ghost stories!"

"It's fun!" Beth said.

So it is. And how would I make my anthology both "fun" and "colorful"? How would I pick the stories to include? My choice was not to choose.

Who better to select the best stories of their states than the people who live there? I sat at my computer, wrote a master letter explaining my intention—to compile favorite and best-known stories from the states—and sent a copy to the archives and state libraries in the capitals of every state in the union. The overwhelming response and gracious cooperation I received went beyond my wildest expectations.

Librarians dug through books, magazines, and newspapers to find tellings of their states' best and most colorful stories. Folklorists and folklore societies helped me identify favorite stories of their states. Magazine editors, publishing houses, and authors kindly granted permission to reprint their copyrighted material. Editors of some of America's leading newspapers actually thanked *me* for including their articles in this anthology. To all of them go my very special thanks, for without their effort, this book would never have made it into print.

This collection, even with my effort to make it as representative as possible of our many cultural heritages, is only a small sampling. It serves to illustrate, though, that Americans love a good ghost story—that they, in fact, love *lots* of good ghost stories. In the pages that follow you'll find, as the title foretells, some *classic American ghost stories*.

Deborah Lynn Downer

Cry Murder

A Suppressed Confession

ON A FLAT UPLAND AREA NEAR the head of Naked Creek was the home of John Perry Bailes. The mention of his name often brought a hush to any conversation among adults and anxiety and fear to the youth who had heard about him. At the fireside on long winter nights, parents related to their children the story how John Perry and two other men had murdered old Ben Lough, but for lack of evidence had never been brought to trial. After the murder, John Perry's alleged accomplices had gone elsewhere to live, but John Perry had remained at the old family homestead where he and his wife, Elvira, kept much to themselves. It was said that shortly before the two men left the community, they met with John Perry in a secret rendezvous where the three took an oath that if any one of them ever confessed to the crime, or implicated the others, it would be the sworn duty of the other two to kill him.

Because of John Perry's crippled condition—his left leg had been severed at the knee in a sawmill accident some years before—he did little farming but made his living largely by buying and selling cattle. This usually meant long trips on horseback for him because the people of his community refused to deal with him.

Many times the people who lived along Naked Creek saw John Perry return from a buying trip, riding ahead of a herd of young calves with strange men as drovers walking behind them. He sat astride his horse in a peculiar manner with his body leaning far forward, the foot of his good leg in a stirrup while his wooden pegleg pointed to the front in a dipping, wagging motion. From his back pocket protruded a large black billfold which was attached to a gold chain that extended from his belt. The wide brim of his soft black hat waggled with the jog of his horse and in unison with the bobbing of his wooden leg.

One night when John Perry was riding up the road about three miles below his house, the ghost of old man Lough came out from the bushes and leaped astride behind him. He tried to elude the ghost by making his horse gallup at full speed. On and on they raced through the night until the horse's sides were covered with sweat and lather and bloody froth dripped from its mouth, but the ghost still sat behind him. On arriving at his front gate, John Perry leaped to the ground, hobbled inside the house and hurriedly locked the door.

"Mercy me, John Perry," Elvira exclaimed. "You look as if you'd seen a ghost!"

John Perry covered his face with his hands as he leaned against the wall and moaned, "I did, Virey, I did!"

Soon everybody in the whole community was talking about how the ghost of old Ben Lough was chasing John Perry Bailes. Time after time it rode home with him which so unnerved him he felt he could bear it alone no longer. In the midst of a revival meeting then being held at the Pine Grove Church, John Perry came in and, much to everyone's surprise, limped up the aisle to the mourners' bench. While the congregation sat in stunned silence, he nervously wrung his hands and jabbered incoherently. Then abruptly he turned and hobbled down the aisle toward the door, his wooden leg striking the bare wood floor with a noise that echoed throughout the sepulchral stillness of the church.

Soon from the woods at the side of the church came the voice of a man praying. The mournful voice grew louder and louder and became so doleful it brought a hush over the congregation. From the pulpit the minister intoned: "The way of transgressors is hard." Then looking toward the woods from which the praying voice came, he said: "I say unto you, John Perry Bailes, there is no forgiveness without repentence, and there is no repentence without full confession." From the congregation came a chorus of Amens.

John Perry did not return to the church and was never seen again by most of the people of the community; nor did they hear anything about him for several weeks. Then it was reported that he was seriously ill with a fever—a fever so high his breath was said to have scorched the varnish on the head-board of his bed.

What little information the people got about his condition came mostly through Elvira's sister, Amanda. She was known throughout the community for her brusque, outspoken manner, no matter what the situation might be. On one of her visits to her brother-in-law's home, she peered down at him and matter-of- factly stated: "John Perry, it 'pears to me you're pert nigh the end of your bean row. From what I've heerd about you and from what I see now, I'd say it's time for you to 'fess up. If you don't, jest as sure as God made little green apples, he'll march you straight through the gates of hell when you die."

When John Perry became worse, it was reported that he had asked for a minister to come to his bedside, presumably to hear a deathbed confession. Suddenly his two former associates appeared and stated that they had come to help take care of John Perry during his illness and thus relieve Elvira of the whole burden of caring for him. From that point on, no one was permitted to enter his room, not even Elvira nor the minister when he came.

Through the long gray afternoon and evening of that chilly November day and far into the night, no sounds came from John Perry's bedroom. Just as the clock on the mantel-piece was striking the hour of three in the morning, the bedroom door opened; then the two men appeared and solemnly announced that he was dead.

Immediately after John Perry's funeral, the two men again left the community never to return. It was generally believed by the people of the community that John Perry had wanted to confess his part in the murder of Ben Lough but his partners in the crime had suppressed it.

"A Supressed Confession" by James Gay Jones originally appeared in *Appalachian Ghost Stories and Other Tales*, McClain Printing Company, Parson, West Virginia, pp. 37-40.

The Ghost of Peddler's Run

A FAMILIAR FIGURE IN THE Colonies during the Eighteenth Century was the itinerant peddler who traveled on foot from village to village and from farmhouse to farmhouse. He carried all sorts of merchandise in a huge pack on his back—such articles as cheap jewelry, shoe buckles, sewing materials and the like. And he usually carried in his hand a stout staff or cane, the threefold purpose of which was to assist him in his walking, to support his heavy pack when he paused to rest without the necessity of removing it from his back, and to beat off vicious dogs.

It was while doing some research recently in the early history of Harford county in preparation for a talk to be given before the County Historical Society that I came upon an eerie tale concerning a peddler and his pack and his staff.

The story begins in 1763. On a spring morning of that year one John Bryarley, who owned and operated a grist mill on Rocky Run, a tributary of the Susquehanna River just above the present Conowingo, was proceeding along a path which led to his mill. As the path paralleled the mill-race and approached quite close to the mill, he saw a figure huddled on the ground not far before him. Running to the figure he was horrified to find that it was the headless body of a man. Although considerably shaken, Bryarley could see that the head had been cut off apparently by one good clean stroke; there were no ragged edges and even the bone of the neck had been neatly cut through. A heavy sharp weapon had been used evidently. The head was nowhere to be found. Bryarley, with the help of several neighbors and the local parson, buried the body in a rough box beside the path where he had found it and erected a stone to mark the grave.

No one knew who the murdered man could be, for without doubt he had been murdered. Then, at berry-picking time, in a thicket not far from where the headless body had been found, a peddler's staff and the top of a peddler's bag were discovered. These clues caused people to reach back into their memories, and it was recalled that on the evening preceding the finding of the body two peddlers had been seen in the neighborhood and had, in fact, stopped for some refreshment at the tavern at Castleman. One was tall and slender and carried a heavy pack on his back and a stout staff in his hand; the other was shorter and powerfully built and carried only a small bag although a heavy cutlass was hanging from his belt. There was no doubt that the shorter peddler had murdered his tall companion for the treasures that he carried in his pack. The cover had probably come off the pack in whatever shuffle there was. But what had become of the murdered man's head?

The summer passed into fall and John Bryarley was hurrying home from his mill one evening, in that period of the day between sundown and nightfall, when he saw in the gathering dusk a tall slender figure bending over at the stone which marked the grave of the peddler. The figure seemed to be poking into the ground with a long stick. As Bryarley approached, the figure straightened and Bryarley saw that it was a man with no head. The headless man ran down the path away from Bryarley toward a small swamp a hundred yards or so distant. Here it again poked at the ground with the stick which it carried and disappeared into the deepening gloom. Bryarley was, of course, a badly frightened man.

But Bryarley was not the only one to see the headless figure, who came to be known as the headless ghost of Peddler's Run, for the name of Rocky Run had thus been changed and remains so today. Other residents of the countryside, using the path along the mill-race, reported seeing the figure at dusk. And it always went through the same motions as it had on the first occasion of Bryarley's seeing it. The figure bent over the grave, poking at the ground, and then ran down the path to the swamp where it repeated this procedure before disappearing into the darkness.

The headless ghost became notorious in that part of the county and people began giving the locality of Bryarley's mill-race a wide berth. Business for the mill fell off and, eventually, Bryarley had to close up and move elsewhere. The mill fell into disrepair and the path along the mill-race grew up in weeds. No one knew whether the ghost still performed his strange antics for no one came this way.

With the passing of time, the land along Peddler's Run remained idle. And then, a discovery was made which recalled the story of the headless ghost and which provided a fitting climax for the story. It was in 1843, 80 years after the murder.

Joseph Warner, a farmer who owned the land formerly occupied by the mill, was digging a drainage ditch from the small swamp to the stream. Suddenly his shovel struck something hard and solid in the soft, yielding mud. Carefully excavating around the object, he uncovered a human skull, buried some 4 feet deep below the surface. Warner removed the skull. The peddler's head had been found.

With the discovery of the skull, the murder which had occurred in the distant past was remembered. Warner disinterred the bones of the luckless peddler and, with due ceremony, reburied them in a new oaken casket with the head properly in place.

And thus was laid the ghost of Peddler's Run. For he was seen no more. His strange motions of poking at the grave with a long stick—it was really a peddler's staff—and running to the swamp to poke at the spot where the head reposed was simply to tell the passerby of his headless plight and how it could be rectified. When the head was reunited with the remains of the rest of the body, the spirit of the peddler rested in peace.

"The Ghost of Peddler's Run" by John T. Stark originally appeared in *The Baltimore Sun*, Baltimore, Maryland, December 20, 1954.

Not His Brother's Keeper

SIXTY YEARS AGO, TWO BROTHERS in a famous Idaho mining area had a pert thirteen-year-old sister who was in school. She was known as a mischief maker. In any case, she reported one day that her teacher had made insulting remarks to her. The girl's father called on him, and the teacher vehemently denied the charge and said he would be willing to go before the trustees. There the matter rested for some time.

But one day the two brothers were seen coming into town, one riding and the other walking, and when the teacher in the hotel barroom was warned, he seized a rifle and went to the porch to meet them. The brother who was walking hid behind the mule and leveled his gun and shot the teacher squarely between the eyes; whereupon with no hesitation at all, he turned and shot his own brother in the stomach. It was argued later that he intended to make out that the teacher had shot his brother, and so justify his murder of the teacher.

The brother shot in the stomach did not die at once. The other came to him one night and said, "It's just too blamed bad that worthless teacher shot you." The sick man shook his head and answered: "No, he didn't shoot me. It was you." The wounded brother died; and the other, after standing trial, was acquitted. Thereupon he fled to Texas and the remainder of this story is legendary. It is said that he was obsessed by the notion that two men were on his trail; and one day, unable any longer to endure his fear and agony of soul, he looked in a mirror and shot himself between the eyes.

"Not His Brother's Keeper" originally appeared in *Idaho Lore*, prepared by the Federal Writer's Project of the Work Projects Administration, The Caxton Printers, Ltd., Caldwell, Idaho, 1939, pp. 53-54. Reprinted by AMS Press, Inc., New York, New York, 1975.

The Night Call

QUITE PURPOSELY, IT SEEMED to the doctor, the stranger stood in the late night shadows outside, his hat pulled low, his face obscured. In a hollow voice, he said that the emergency was south, below the new homes down Flores and Presa Streets.

That he was about to embark on a house call that he would never forget, and to venture into a yet-unexplained mystery, did not occur to the young San Antonio physician. His was the new century of the 1900s, a promising practice in this growing little city of fifty thousand souls, and a pretty young wife—altogether a good life.

And a fine night, this one—soft with a lowering moon and the green scent of spring. Certainly it was late, but let his wife join him—he'd hitch the buggy.

He turned to reassure the stranger who had come knocking at their door, but the man had retreated into the dark at the hitching post and was already saddled. Silent, he waited there, then led away down South Presa, where only a few lamplit windows still watched the night.

"What's wrong with him?" The doctor's wife seemed uneasy. "He's so withdrawn."

"His friend's hurt; he's worried. You could tell it in his voice. With night calls, they're always worried."

"But the way he was dressed? So...well, old fashioned."

The physician flicked his reins to keep up; the horseman was indistinct in the night ahead of them. "I didn't notice; he stayed in the shadows."

They had come farther than the doctor had expected. The

fine two-story houses had thinned to scattered frame bunga-lows; then the cobbled paving stopped, and off to the east, the dark line of river timber crept closer. Now the shadowy rider took a narrow side road leading into those trees.

It was dark beneath—clouds had scudded across the moon. They scarcely saw the man dismount, for suddenly the house loomed. Deep in the trees it stood—some square columns, a broad front gallery, some gabled windows—all of it vaguely brooding.

As though part of their surrounding shadows, the man stood motionless within a near grove of oaks; without speaking, he pointed toward one dimly-lighted window. The physician, with deliberate effort, put down an uneasiness that was grow-ing; he spoke quietly to his wife. She should stay in the buggy.

He mounted the steps to the porch and found the front door ajar. The lighted room was just off the entrance hall, so dark he could distinguish nothing within it. Bag in hand, he entered the dim room.

He was not prepared for what awaited him. Blood, in gouts and spatters, seemed everywhere; a chair, its leg broken off, sagged in the corner. To the doorway where he stood, a bloody trail led from a bed across the room; a table beside it had been overturned.

On the bed, a young woman lay still, watching him. Under her right kneecap was a smear of blood. She was naked.

Even with the woman before him and his thoughts racing, the mind of a physician prevailed—someone had just died here. Death was violent—the feel of it seeping in from the dark all about...a violence yet impending.

The woman was wounded; he must treat her. She was naked; someone should be with him—his wife? He turned toward the window, and a voice challenged from the darkness beyond: "Leave her out here!"

He opened his bag and bent over the woman on the bed.

The wound was slight; he treated and bandaged it, working rapidly. Silent, the woman's eyes remained on him. He felt them, though he could not even hear her breathe.

"It's not too bad," he said without looking up; a bullet had grazed her. Feeling the hair crawl along his neck, he hurried to finish, from the corner of his eye, he had glimpsed a face at the window—momentarily there, then gone.

As he later remembered, he told the woman to come to his office in the morning; he would re-dress the wound. Without speaking, she had nodded. It was only when he turned at the door that he realized how extraordinarily pretty she was. Then the deadliness of the room and the sense of imminent violence beset him again, and he plunged into the dark hall and safely through it.

He forced himself not to run for his buggy. Then he was in it, almost unaware that from somewhere in the shadows, money had been thrust into his hand. He reined around, feeling his wife trembling, and he looked back only once as he whipped the horse.

Night had swallowed the house—the light at that solitary window, extinguished.

His wife had been desperately afraid; a man had watched him from the window. Not the one who had come to their home: he had stayed in the trees, watching the buggy. She thought the man at the window had a gun.

He told her what he had seen. Someone had been murdered and dragged out.

Then he must go to the police. His wife spoke more calmly; they were back within the city's lamplight.

Two days passed while he told himself he was waiting for the young woman to come for an examination. She would never come. His wife was right; he went to the police.

There was nothing at that address, a deputy told him—just an old house that hadn't been occupied in years. It was not old, the doctor insisted; he had been there.

Anyway, it was not the house, it was that room! He would show them.

In the end, two officers went with him. There was no mistaking the lonely road nor the house, almost as shadowy by day as he remembered it.

But that was all that he had remembered rightly. It was a sagging wreck of abandonment.

The room! The bed was there, and the chair and bedside table. A coverlet lay on the bed, unstained. Everywhere, dust spread an undisturbed mantle. The doctor rubbed his eyes—this had been the slaughterhouse room!

There were stains on the flooring that had been scrubbed many times...and long ago. The gallery sagged as they came out, for the deputy there had called to them. He hurried over, shaking his head in disbelief.

All at once, in that closest grove of trees, a man had been watching him. There was blood all over his face, and his shirt was soaked with it. As the deputy had started for him, the man had disappeared.

"Not twenty feet from me, plain as day," the deputy said. "Then he vanished!"

They prowled all through the trees toward the river; nothing was there.

Returning to town, the doctor put his question hesitantly—did they believe what he had told them? To himself he admitted that he was no longer sure of what he had seen.

The officers remained noncommittal. They would come again tomorrow and look around more closely. The deputy knew what he had seen—a dead man still on his feet.

The doctor did not return; the officers did, and shortly thereafter, closed their investigation. There was talk—secondhand, as is the way with such talk—that all three of them came back, and all saw the bloody figure waiting in the grove once more. Among themselves, they agreed it best to leave that part unmentioned.

As to the house, what else but to report it still as empty as it had been for so many years?

And so the case remained closed, for in short months, a flood took the ruin away. Where its foundations had stood, some said that a grave-sized hole remained. Others thought the grave was nearer the trees by the house...but floodwaters do strange things to bottom land.

Some say, even today, that the doctor's descendants still possess three silver dollars—payment for a late night house call.

However, who can be sure? Doctors have a rule—they must never talk about the patients they have seen.

"The Night Call" by William Edward Syers originally appeared in *Ghost Stories of Texas*, Texian Press, Waco, Texas, 1981, pp. 8-11.

Loves Lost

Willie and Nellie: A Love Story

AT THE CORNER OF Bull and Oglethorpe Streets in the heart of Savannah's downtown historic district stands an elegant Regency townhouse which many of the townspeople simply call the Birthplace. It was here on October 31, 1860, a night, as she later wrote, "associated with All Halloween, fairies, imps, and witches," that Juliette Gordon, founder of the Girl Scouts of the U.S.A., was born to Nellie and William Washington Gordon, II.

Just as the Gordon home stands proudly on its crossroads corner, the family has been prominent in Savannah for nearly two centuries. The first Gordons in America settled in New Jersey prior to the Revolution, where part of the battle of Monmouth was fought on their family farm. After the war Ambrose Gordon found his way to Georgia, and named his first son William Washington after his old commanding officer, a nephew of the first president. Elizabeth, wife of Ambrose, is also known in Savannah history as a spirited woman who defied the government ban on trade with England during the War of 1812. She is said to have shipped her cotton down the Savannah River while sitting on top of the bales in a rocking chair, hoping the soldiers would be too chivalrous to fire at a woman.

Their son William was the first Georgian ever to be graduated from West Point. He was also a founder of the Central of Georgia Railroad, and the first Gordon to live in the house.

The handsome pink stucco home, which was to become Savannnah's first National Historic Landmark, was built about 1820 for Judge Moore Wayne, later an associate justice of the Supreme Court, and William's uncle by marriage.

The Gordon's bought the Wayne home when the judge left for Washington. Here their son William, II was born, and here he brought his bride, Nellie Kinzie, in 1858. Those who walk through the house museum, now the Juliette Gordon Low Girl Scout National Center, today find the house restored as it was during Juliette's childhood. It is also rich in family mementos and the feel of a home which knew five generations of Gordons, and a great deal of love.

Beyond the story of Juliette, founder of the scout movement in America and a truly liberated woman of her time, was the tender love story of her parents. They knew the lasting happiness denied Juliette in her marriage to Willy Low, son of a wealthy cotton broker, and playboy friend of English nobility.

It is said that Willie Gordon first decided to marry Nellie, an eighteen-year-old schoolmate of his sister Eliza, in 1853 when she slid down the main staircase of the Yale Library at New Haven where Willie was a student, and crushed his new hat. She maintained the habit of sliding down staircases, along with other high-spirited ways, until her last illness in her house in 1917, when the doctor had told her not to use the stairs.

Her ancestry, as sturdy as his, was an interesting mixture of Puritan New Englanders and frontier pioneers, including some of the founders of the city of Chicago. Her grandmother, Eleanor Lytle, had once been captured by the Indian Chief Cornplanter, who gave her the nickname, "Little Ship Under Full Sail." It became an affectionate term also within the family for both Nellie and Juliette.

In marrying, both Willie and Nellie made some compromises. She was troubled by slavery, but accepted his loyalty to the South. He gave up his Presbyterian membership for her Episcopalian faith. Their disparate backgrounds were soon an issue in what Nellie called The Confederate War. Willie served with the Georgia Hussars, and was wounded at the battle of Atlanta. Nellie lost one brother, John, in the Union service, and had two brothers captured. Even closer home, her uncle General David Hunter was in charge of the troops who took Fort Pulaski just outside of Savannah in 1862.

During the War, Nellie was to involve both Generals, Robert

E. Lee and W.T. Sherman, in helping her find her Willie at different times, a record even for her. First, she went to locate her husband in Virginia, where the Confederate leader gallantly gave her an escort of two soldiers. The couple shared a brief reunion before Nellie hurried back to Savannah to hide her family silver and valuables before the arrival of the Federal forces.

After the capture of Savannah, General Sherman came to call, delivering some mail from her family and giving the children their first candy and sugar. His band played "When This Cruel War is Over," outside the house as he promised to put a guard over the residence. All Confederate officers' wives were being ordered to leave the city. In Nellie's case, General Sherman complied with her request to be allowed to go with a flag of truce into South Carolina, to say goodbye to Willie before she and the children left by steamer from Hilton Head for the north.

After their wartime separation, the Gordons returned to Savannah in 1865. Three more children, a total of six in all, were born in the house, and Willie became president of the Savannah Cotton Exchange. Willie later served his country during the Spanish American War, when he was commissioned a brigadier general. Nellie went with him to his command in Miami, and gained national recognition for her work in soldiers' relief. On one occasion, when she learned that a group of sick men had been placed on a train in Florida bound for their homes without nurses or medicine, she went with them herself all the way to Indiana, dosing them with milk punch and brandy.

President William McKinley paid tribute to them both; his successor, William Howard Taft, kept a parade waiting as their house guest in 1909 while he enjoyed lively conversation, waffles and venison in their dining room.

When Nellie visited her daughters Juliette and Mabel in England, Rudyard Kipling put her in a story as "a little old lady with snapping black eyes, who used very bad language," an honor for which she immediately thanked him.

When Willie died in 1912, flags flew at half-staff in Savannah. His own Georgia Hussars escorted his body to Laurel

Grove Cemetery. Nellie's children feared for her mental state as Juliette wrote her brother Arthur, "She never pretended for a moment that he was not her first and last love, and we as nothing in comparison. I believe Papa thought that the triumph of his life! Maternal love is the inheritance of the ages, but love such as Mamma gave him, was a personal tribute."

Among the many volumes of Nellie's in the Gordon library, there is one on spiritualism. We do not know what Nellie thought of its theories, so widely discussed in the late nineteenth century. At eighty-one, she wrote a cousin: "My strict observance of the Fifth Commandment has resulted in my 'living long in the land' according to the promise...unless it is because the Lord doesn't want me, and the Devil doesn't want me, either. At any rate, here I remain, very much against my will, for there is nothing I so sincerely desire in this world as to get out of it."

During her last illness, she said to her daughter-in-law Ellie, "When I die, I don't want anybody to wear mourning. I don't want any tears...I shall be so happy to be with my Willie again, everyone should celebrate."

Nellie died in the big front bedroom of her home on Washington's birthday, February 22, 1917. At the moment of her death, her five living children were with her. Her daughter-in-law Margaret, who had already said her own goodbye to the frail, fiery little woman, was sitting quietly in an adjoining bedroom, which had been General Gordon's.

As she waited there, according to an account written by her daughter Mary Stewart Gordon Platt, she was surprised to see a familiar figure. The general, wearing his familiar grey suit, was just coming out of his wife's bedroom. His expression, wrote Mrs. Platt, was "one of grave gladness." He walked through his old room and down the front stairs.

In a few minutes, Arthur, Margaret's husband, appeared to tell her that his mother was gone. Together they walked down the stairs. Margaret had attempted to tell Arthur what she had seen, but he had gently told her she was only over-wrought, and perhaps had dozed off as she waited. She said no more as they reached the front hallway. There the old family butler was waiting, tears streaming down his worn cheeks.

Before they could speak, he told the same story. He had seen the general, in the grey suit, walk down the stairs just as he always did, and out the front door, "same as allus when de buggy been waiting for him dere," Mrs. Platt quotes him as saying. "Lawd, 'twas good ter see him again...He look so well and happy...happier den I mos' ever seed him...I thought you lake to know de General come fetch her hisself, suh."

Daisy Gordon Lawrence, a niece of Juliette's who later wrote her aunt's biography, *Lady From Savannah*, with Gladys Denny Shultz, also says of Nellie's last moments: "Her children say that when she died, her face took on the radiance of a bride, going to meet her bridegroom."

Nellie Gordon: A Postscript

Although most people today think of the Juliette Gordon Low Girl Scout National Center as a happy and peaceful place, full of the tourists and Girl Scouts from all over the world who enjoy its Victorian decor and Gordon family antiques, some staff members say that when they are alone in the building, the impressions of the founder's family are still evident. This especially seems to take the form of footsteps on the stairs and through the rooms after the center is closed.

A guide there told me that she had once caught a fleeting and unexpected glimpse of Juliette's mother, Nellie Kinzie Gordon, one afternoon after the woman had just completed her last tour of the day. "I was getting ready to go home," she recalled. "The house was quiet, the lights out. Just as they were locking the door, I remembered a book I had left upstairs. I asked the woman with the keys to please wait for me while I went to get it.

"As she stood in the garden, I stepped inside the back entrance, and hurried up the stairs. I didn't turn on the lights. It was still daylight, but getting a little dim, as it was a late Sunday afternoon in the winter. Well, suddenly I heard a kind of rustle, and a figure was there above me, in the center hall. I recognized Mrs. Gordon from the picture in the library.

"I don't know who was the most startled. She drew back as though to say, 'Oh, I thought you'd all gone!' I turned and hurried down the stairs without my book, or even looking back. When I finally did glance back, at the door, she was gone. It was as though she had simply been waiting to get her house back."

Incidents have also been reported at the Center of long-lost items suddenly turning up in plain sight, and being moved about when the museum is closed. Both Eddie, the maintenance man, and my friend Stephen have heard the faint, far-away sound of a pianoforte playing, recalling the fact that Mrs. Gordon was an accomplished musician. "The instrument which we now have here in the north parlor only has about 20 percent of its keys in working order, but the one which we hear," added Stephen, "is perfectly in tune."

Eddie says that he has frequently caught a glimpse of Mrs. Gordon, "wearing a long blue robe, with flowers all over it," at the dining room table when he comes in early in the morning.

"Sometimes," he says, "I feel as though the whole family were present, just watching me, and then continues 'life as usual' when we all go home...especially with the house so much as it was when they were all here."

"Willie and Nellie: A Love Story" by Margaret Wayt DeBolt originally appeared in *Savannah Spectres and Other Strange Tales*, Donning Co. Publishers, Norfolk, Virginia, 1984, pp. 61-68.

The Mourning Bride: She is Gone Forever from Historic Old Glendale Station

THE GHOSTLY BRIDE OF GLENDALE is gone forevermore. The wooden porch on which she awaited her tardy lover burned away many years ago and disappeared from mortal eyes.

Now the whirr of tires has driven her away for good, for legend has it that she is visible only to travelers on horseback.

The story of the ghostly bride has been revived with the development of cattle ranches near Glendale and increasing traffic over an improved road that passes by the shell of what once was a bustling stagecoach station. This is where the bride waited.

All that remains of the station today is a desolate sentinel in stone high on the eastern bank of Beaver creek in Fremont county. The station, on the old Granite-Colorado City stage-coach route, is in an angular, sharply gabled two-story house of four-foot native gray stone walls. The walls have withstood the elements since the seventies.

Time was when a great cluster of barns and corrals stretched away from the house above the creekbed and 1,000 head of mules and horses were sheltered there to furnish exchange teams for the heavy traffic of those exciting gold rush days.

Old-timers of the Beaver park district say J.H. McClure, who came to Canon City in the early 60's, built this house. He later built a hotel in Canon City which is today known as the Strathmore.

The house was built for a hostelry to accommodate travelers and drivers of the stagecoach road built by Bob Spotswood and William McClelland in 1873 for stage and express. Leaving Colorado City, the stagecoach road followed closely the base of Cheyenne mountain and out across the outlying plains much as the paved highway does now.

The old road turned from the route of the main highway of today at Hitch-Rack ranch and went west by Lyttle, coming out at Sullivan park along Red creek. It continued to Glendale, which stands at the junction of Beaver and Red creeks.

This stagecoach line was started as the result of the discovery of gold in Colorado. As Denver flourished such routes were heavily traveled and accommodations were needed along the way. The slow-moving oxen which brought the adventurers to the west were soon discarded for the fast, handsome horses on the stagecoaches, and to keep the coaches moving change stations were established. Glendale was one of them.

When the magnitude of the Leadville discoveries was recognized the traffic became enormous and 100 passengers or more were served daily at Glendale station.

It was in these romantic boom days preceding the coming of the railroad that Glendale reached its peak of glory.

The Glendale building had been well made. It was built for permanency with double stone walls handhewn from adjacent quarries. It boasted ornate porticos which graced the front and one side of the building on both the upper and lower stories.

There were well-kept lawns, flower-lined walks and a picnic grove of cottonwoods on the other side of the creek.

The front door opened into a spacious hall with an attractive winding staircase. Two large parlors, heated by mammoth fireplaces, were upon each side of the hall. In days gone by these richly-furnished rooms furnished the locale for weddings, parties, dances and gospel devotions.

Scouts stopped there for news. Trappers, in leather-fringed jackets, paused on their way down the Arkansas river. Indians camped nearby and cowhands up from Texas, with their colorful dress and lazy drawl, gave color to the popular place.

The station hummed with life night and day. Here were

travelers of all classes; the gentle-woman in her silks and shawl, the dance hall hostess in her gaudy raiment, the gamblers seeking new-rich cities and the miner hoping to have some share of the riches in the silver mines. Here were the mingled smells of cedar logs and knots of pitch pine, of lavender and rare perfumes, of newly baked bread and roast venison from the kitchen, the dust of the open road.

Here passed the man who had made his stake and the eager travelers seeking theirs, a constant stream going and coming, lingering for the night and on their way again with the dawn.

Many were the tales exchanged about the yawning fire-places on wintry nights when men of vision told of their dreams. Some spoke only of gold and silver but others, who spoke less loudly, told of their hopes for farms and cattle and grain.

The most conspicuous figure, perhaps was the stage driver, resplendent in his broadcloth and silk, shiny leather gloves and his high boots. He told his stories in a loud voice. He was proud of his work and held the most exalted position of anyone working along the line.

But there was a romantic sadness in his voice when he spoke of the new lines being built by the railroads, and a wistful note of anxiety crept into his words as he marked the progress made by the railroad nearing Canon City and planning to go on to Leadville.

If anyone suggested that stagecoaches might become a thing of the past, he would become suddenly quiet and if they would offer the idea that he might drive a train sometime, he would bluster in indignation.

But the day came when the rattle and clatter of the stage-coach was heard no more and the proud, haughty driver was not needed and Glendale was deserted. Today the gaunt build-ing stands alone, dreaming.

Its front porches have disappeared, the mountain grasses have crept down and taken over the lawns.

Loneliness is on all sides but there is still an air of dignity about the place and although the windows stare vacantly down the valley, there is something commanding about the building.

Glendale station lost practically all its old identifying marks almost in the twinkling of an eye on the night of June 3, 1921, when the flood waters of Red and Beaver creeks joined in one gigantic wall and rolled from the creek bed over the high banks where the buildings stood, carrying everything before. Only the house remained intact. This same flood went on to Pueblo where it wrecked a part of that city and claimed many lives.

The story of the ghostly bride is told by oldtimers who say they knew of lonely horseback riders who saw her fragile figure standing on the porch, her wedding veil fluttering about her shoulders as she watched them ride by in the moonlight.

She was a beautiful girl, the daughter of one of the landlords of Glendale and she lived at the time when the station was at the height of its fame and glory.

It was at one of the station's gay parties that the girl met and fell in love with a dashing young gentlemen from the south who was seeking his fortune in the gold fields.

The man also loved the girl and she promised to wait for his return.

He came back some months later and plans were made for the wedding. Even the day was set. Then back he went to the mines for more wealth and one day word came to her that he would be at Glendale on the appointed day.

The wedding was planned for that evening. Guests were present. Lights shone from every window and a sumptuous wedding supper was ready to be served. The bridegroom and two companions were to arrive from Canon City.

But the supper hour came and no bridegroom appeared. The anxious girl watched the roadway from a porch which commanded a view of the road on which her lover should come.

For a long time she stood there in her white satin wedding gown, the trailing veil held to her dark brown hair. It was moonlight and she could see down the road for some distance.

She knew he was coming horseback and she listened for the sound of hoofs upon the rock-strewn road. But no rider appeared and finally she gave way to despair and grief and her friends helped her to her room.

At last a party of men mounted their horses and went in

search of the tardy bridegroom. They found that he had been murdered and robbed of his gold, possibly by his companions. His horse stood beside him and it bore his lifeless body to the waiting bride.

A short time later the heartbroken young woman became ill and died. For many years, the story goes, travelers making the trip by horseback on moonlit nights swore they could see her waiting figure on the upper porch. Her white satin gown would glow in the moonlight and her wedding veil would flutter about her head and shoulders with every passing breeze.

Some riders even said they could hear her sweet voice calling, and then a heartbreaking sob just before she would disappear.

Her ghostly figure was only seen by horseback riders as they approached the house. The click of the horseshoes upon the stones seemed to call her spirit back to watch for her faithful lover.

"The Mourning Bride" by Janet Sterling originally appeared in *The Denver Post*, August 10, 1947.

The Ghostly Romance of the Old Beckwith Manor: How the Cavalier George Beckwith Returned To His Home From Over the Sea

WASHINGTON, OCT. 6—IN 1648 Nicholas Hervey, a near relative of the governor of Virginia of that name and a member of the General Assembly of Maryland, received from London a land grant of 1,000 acres lying on the south shore of the Patuxent, then in Calvert and now in St. Mary's county.

He was a bluff old soldier, who had fought in the wars in Flanders. He was commissioned by Lord Baltimore a captain to prevent the encroachment of the Indians upon the new settlements. He built himself a home in a beautiful cove at the mouth of Town Creek, on a sloping hill overlooking the Patuxent river and Chesapeake bay. The bricks he used were imported as ballast from the mother country. Here he married and lived, respected by all, for many years. He served the Province in the General Assembly, and at his house the courts met. He had one child, a daughter Frances, who, growing to womanhood, was wooed and won by a newcomer to the colony, George Beckwith, "gentleman and planter," as stated in the old records at Annapolis.

George Beckwith, who had emigrated to the Province but shortly before, was the scion of one of the oldest and one of the most prominent families of Yorkshire, Eng. It was a love match, and it was the custom of the lovers, in the gloaming of the evening, to sit beneath the spreading elm on the slope of the hill overlooking the bay. They had four children, a son and three daughters, whose descendants are to be found in Maryland and other states at the present time. Urgent business recalled Beckwith to Yorkshire in 1675, and the family, friends, neighbors, and workmen of the plantation all congregated at the landing to bid the husband, father, friend, and master all-speed.

The vessel, with sails ready set, had its anchor in the offing. The small boat, manned by four robust slaves of the plantation, with oars raised, waited the last word. As the godspeeds were all said, the husband, taking his wife in his arms, said in a loud voice so that all could hear: "Do not weep, sweetheart, for, living or dead, I shall come back to you." The oars dipped into the water, and the little boat grew fainter and fainter, and the vessel sailed out into the Chesapeake and was soon lost in the mists of the sea.

There were but few colonists in those days, settlements were widely scattered, and but few vessels put into the Patuxent with news from the mother country. Months passed away, and still no word came from the husband and father. The disconsolate wife and mother at dusk each evening took her seat beneath the elm and expectantly waited the return of her beloved. As days passed a visible change took place, and gradually she became more frail, and at last was laid away in the little graveyard a few rods up the hill. The orphans, minors, were placed under the care of the State, and a guardian was appointed for them.

It was not long before a slight and misty figure was seen, dressed all in somber black, seated beneath the elm on the lawn on moonlight nights, gazing out into the dim distance of the bay, and as darkness drew on it would slowly vanish. Whence she came and whither she went none knew, possibly back to her resting place in the little graveyard on the hill. Months had rolled into two years, when, on a bright moonlight night, the lights of a large ship were seen entering the Patuxent. More and more distinct became the form of a majestic ship of the sea with every sail in place, of ghostly whiteness. The news soon spread from plantation to plantation, and many persons assembled at the landing place expecting the homecoming of the husband

and father. The ship came to anchor with all her sails still to leeward—so unnerving a sight a shudder passed over the onlookers. A small boat was seen to leave the vessel, but with only one figure, a tall man wrapped in a long mantle and his broad-brimmed hat, fastened with a single black feather, drawn upon his forehead. Motionless the cavalier stood, until approaching the landing place, the pale handsome features of Beckwith were distinctly seen by all.

A Ghostly Meeting

An awful stillness fell upon the visitors at the wharf. None was prepared to tell him of the death of his wife. A gentle wind from the direction of the mansion on the hill was felt, and all involuntarily turning in that direction, saw approaching the figure of his wife. The figure of the husband and father sprang upon the landing and clasping his ghostly wife in his arm, in a loud voice said: "As promised, sweetheart, living or dead, I have returned," and as the startled onlookers looked again, cavalier, lady, boat and vessel had all disappeared. It was shortly afterward learned from an incoming vessel that George Beckwith had died in London the year before.

In the long 250 years that have followed the two figures of cavalier and lady have frequently been seen standing beneath the elm tree, always in somber black, their eyes always directed toward the pathway of incoming vessels. Lately cavalier and lady have reappeared, all dressed in courtly fashion, in spotless white and flashing jewels, always standing beneath the elm on the lawn, still gazing seaward as if in expectation of a coming guest.

The plantation passed into other hands, and the old brick house, long since in ruins, was, about 1858, cleared away, and the then owner commenced to build a modern home upon the old foundations. Hardly had the framework been placed and weather boarded than strange noises were heard. The building was abandoned and the house is still empty. There is an old tradition in the family that never will the old plantation home be inhabited until a descendant of George and Frances Beckwith becomes the owner. Then the manor house will be rebuilt and the old plantation will again bloom in old-time style, taking its former place among the baronial manors of Maryland.

"The Ghostly Romance of the Old Beckwith Manor" by Paul Beckwith originally appeared in *The Baltimore Sun*, Baltimore, Maryland, October 7, 1906.

Savannah's Sweetheart of Mankind

FOR 44 YEARS, YEAR IN AND year out, the favorite game of people traveling into the Savannah harbor was to wave to the lovely girl standing in front of her home on Elba Island, near the lighthouse. By day she waved a white apron and by night she waved a lantern; it was rare indeed if anyone traveling that way didn't get a friendly wave. Where else in the world do you get friendliness like this? the seamen asked. Where else in the world? But Florence Martus was not flapping her apron in the breeze only to bear goodwill. She truly hoped one of the seamen would be her fiance, who had sailed away and promised to return to her.

Sometime in the late nineteenth century, she bade farewell to her fiance as he sailed away. She made a solemn promise that she would greet every ship that passed the lighthouse until he returned. He would see her as he sailed by, and he would know that she had waited for him. Each time a vessel approached, she ran from the house in her flat-heeled, two-button shoes, holding her apron high in the air. All hands on board waved back, and some of them called greetings to her. But each ship passed by, going on down the river. Her face did not change expression. Perhaps the next vessel...

During this time, and well into the twentieth century, the only transportation to and from the islands between Charleston, Beaufort and Savannah was by boat. There were boats of all sizes and descriptions, and their cargo usually consisted of potatoes, cabbages, tobacco, beef, corn, and wheat. And, of course, sea island cotton. The cotton was bound into long, narrow bales. When the vessels left the dock, they carried a cargo of Low Country products.

Some of the boats had upper and lower decks, and even staterooms. The larger and more expensive boats had two beds in each stateroom. Most of the officers on the ships, like the purser, captain, and engineer, had wives in Charleston or Beaufort or Savannah. But they blew their whistles at the girl waving her apron. They all loved her, for no person could ever be more friendly or faithful.

And there was always a fishing fleet that went out at first light and came in at dusk. Like a swarm of flies, the small boats swarmed into the harbor, jib and mainsail out, men on deck, whacking away with blades that flashed in the light as they cleaned the day's catch. Seagulls swarmed overhead, screaming for a morsel. Occasionally a sea turtle was on board. When properly cooked, sea turtle was delicious, as were their eggs. Turtle stew was a favorite with seamen.

Florence waved to every ship that passed Elba Island, and she learned the ways of the sea. She created her own little weather station, becoming a student of clouds, wind, surf, and sun. She became an expert on predicting weather patterns. One day all of the signs indicated a terrible hurricane was about to crash on Elba Island. It was likely that the water level would rise to an astonishing level. Although the sun was shining and the sky was clear, Florence spoke to her brother of an impending storm. She decided that when the storm came she would take refuge about halfway up the spiral stairway in an abandoned fort on the island. By the next morning, dark clouds scudded over the sea, and ships were listing in the waves, which were getting higher and higher.

As time passed, the wind blew water so furiously it appeared to be a white froth. Hunks of foam flew through the air. No ships were in sight, so Florence went to the abandoned fort and took her station midway up the spiral stairway. The wind became so swift and strong that no man could have walked in it. The water swept over the bank and began to rise, Florence held tightly to the stairway and prayed that God would let her live at least until her fiance returned. Finally, the wind quietened, and the water began to recede. The storm was over.

Occasionally a ship would dock at Elba Island, and Florence would run down to the dock and speak to the hands. She listened to their talk for hours on end, catching snatches of conversation coming from several groups of seamen who talked at the same time. She never heard a word that concerned her fiance. But that didn't deter her from waving to every boat that passed her little house on Elba Island, 7 1/2 miles below Savannah.

The vigil ended in 1931 when Florence's brother retired from his government job as lighthouse keeper. He had reached the age of 70 and had been the lighthouse keeper since 1887. He and his sister moved away.

In 1938 the Propellor Club had a celebration in honor of Florence. Over 3,000 people attended. A huge birthday cake was decorated with a replica of her home where she had lived on Elba Island. Many state officials attended the celebration, and they chose a fitting title for Florence, whom they had always referred to as the "Sweetheart of Mankind."

A progressive harbor has evolved since the time of Florence Martus, but you can see the statue of Florence waving her apron, her dog at her side, on River Street in Savannah. A plaque by the statue reads:

Florence Martus
1869 - 1943
Savannah's Waving Girl

On another side of the statue, the following words are inscribed:

Her immortality stems from her
friendly greeting to passing ships,
a welcome to strangers entering the
port and a farewell to wave them
safely onward.
The sculpture is by Felix De Weldon, done in 1971.

If you take a cruise and pass Elba Island, gaze devoutly at the island. The waving girl is said to appear from time to time, always waving her apron, trusting that her fiance will return to her.

"Savannah's Sweetheart of Mankind" by Nancy Rhyne originally appeared in *Coastal Ghosts: Haunted Places from Wilmington, North Carolina to Savannah, Georgia*, The East Woods Press, Charlotte, North Carolina, pp. 165-169.

The Spirit of the Spring Waconda

NOTE: The Waconda Spring was flooded in 1965 to form Waconda Lake. Technically, there is no longer a Waconda Spring.

IN EVERY COMMUNITY, AS IN every state, there is some one thing that sets it apart, and makes it just a bit different from any other. But one must study its geography or its history to discover the particular thing that makes it an individual place, just as your eyes, your hair or your smile make you, you, and no one else.

The boys and girls who live in Cawker City have this distinction, this advantage over the rest of us. They have near them a bit of the old Kansas sea. At least it looks as though it might have been a part of the old ocean, for it is salt, sea-green and very, very deep, and seems to rise and fall with the tides, as do the waters in the great seas far away.

When Mother Earth made that last terrific attempt at dressmaking, about a hundred thousand years ago, and folded her too-loose gown into the great wrinkle that piled the Rocky Mountains from two to three miles in the air, the Kansas sea was disturbed. In fact it was quite spilled out of its bed, and started running, willy-nilly, down and around, hither and yon in all directions. In its greatest depths, it left pools which finally dried away to form the top layer of the salt beds of the Hutchinson country. It left in its shallower basins great sandy desert wastes in which the last of the sea-creatures died and became fossils. But most of the water reached the other oceans in the east and south.

47

Out in north central Kansas, however, there was this one little pool which neither dried up nor ran away. Whether it was held by peculiar rock formation, bubbled up from hidden springs, or just stayed of its won accord, I cannot say. Perhaps the Mother Sea left it to watch like an eye over all the changes that were to take place—the dying out of the waterfolk, the passing of the huge land-creatures, the coming of man himself—the transformation of all the old ocean-bed into the grassy plains we know and love.

At any rate, there it is, this little pool of sea-green water. Standing forty or more feet above the valley of the winding Solomon, not far from the river itself, is the rounded hillock which holds the age-old spring. The basin is about fifty feet across at the top, cone-shaped and lined with jagged rocks, which narrow with the descent downward. Deep-sea divers have not been able to explore the bottom, nor have sounding instruments been able to plumb its exact depth. The water itself shows a heavy mineral content, and has been found beneficial in the treatment of various diseases. A sanatorium is located at the spring. The water is used both as a medicine, and for baths. It has not an especially pleasant taste, but how few medicines are really good to take!

The spring seems always ready to overflow, but does not, for the surplus water escapes in seeping springs far down the side of the bluff next to the river. The basin looks like the crater of an ancient volcano, the rocks about it seeming igneous, or fire-formed. But geologists tell us they are just our old Kansas friend, limestone, though with a different grayish color and more porous texture than those tinged with yellow we have seen in so many places.

White men have known this spring for more than a hundred years. Lieutenant Pike is said to have visited it in 1806. But for more years than anyone can tell, the red man knew it, and used it as a shrine. Beads, bows and arrows, French and Spanish medals, even human bones have been brought by divers from its cool green depths. The Indian name for it, Wah-kan-dah, is also their name for spirit. Their legend of it must date far, far back in plains history.

Early settlers of Mitchell County often saw roving bands of hunters, who never passed through that part of the country without holding some sort of pow-wow or religious ceremony at their Spirit Spring. In the very early days of Cawker City a friendly band of Pottawatomies, who were hunting buffalo in the neighborhood, was invited to put on a war-dance before the citizens of the town. They agreed to do so, but insisted that first they must go to Spirit Springs. They daubed their faces and their ponies with the grey mud from the banks, and their appearance, in the weird light of their bonfires, was so fearful that the settlers breathed a sigh of relief when the dance was safely over, and their visitors had departed.

To one of the very old settlers of Mitchell County, a friendly Indian told the legend of Waconda, their Spring of Spirit. It is something as follows.

Waconda was the name of the most beautiful Indian maid, daughter of a chief of one of the plains tribes. Her hair had the blackness and sheen of the blackest of black crow's wings, her eyes were large and dark. The red blood glowed faintly through the brown of her cheeks, and richly crimson in her softly curved lips. She was slender, and not too tall, but with her strong young arms she could send an arrow swift and true, and as straight from the bow as any of the young men in her tribe. Her fringed dress of richly embroidered doeskin she wore with the lithe grace born of her free, wild life on the plains. Her mocassins, skillfully embroidered like her dress with gayly-dyed porcupine quills, tripped over the prairie grass as noiselessly and lightly as did the feet of the shy wild deer. She was the pride of her mother's teepee, the idol of her father's heart, a delight to the eyes of the young men of her tribe, the joy of all her people.

One spring Waconda's father had led his hunting-party into the river valley. The women and children were encamped near the stream, but the hunters had wandered far to the south in search of the northward bound buffalo. Waconda had determined to explore the country, and unafraid, had wandered some distance from the camp. A rocky bluff reared its head high above the rolling plain to the west, and Waconda of the venturesome spirit wished to see what lay beyond it. Cautiously, as even the most daring of Indian maidens would be sure to do, she climbed the rugged face of the cliff. From its summit the hill descended in a gentle slope westward to meet the level plain that stretched out to the edge of the world.

Waconda scanned the landscape with attentive eyes. Her ear caught a sound. She dropped instantly to the ground and listened intently. Yes, it was a human cry, a call for help, and coming from a clump of plum-bushes halfway down the sloping hill. The Indian girl crept forward quietly until she could see the crumpled figure of a man in the scant shade of the shrubbery. She examined the surroundings closely. He was alone. Unafraid now, she rose and ran swiftly to him. His eyes were closed.

"You are hurt. Can I help?" she asked, bending over him. The eyelids lifted wearily.

"Oh, gentle maiden, if I could but have water. I—I am so weak from loss of blood—I—can do nothing."

"A moment and you shall have it." The girl's sharp prairie-trained vision had caught a glimpse of deeper greenness at the foot of the hill. Hurrying to it, she found a trickling spring from which she carried as much water as her deerskin pouch would hold. The young warrior drank gratefully, and tried to lift himself. "No, no, do not move! See the blood starts! I will get more water now, and will bathe and bind your wounds," said practical Waconda. She bandaged as skillfully as she was able the deep cuts in arm and thigh from which so much blood had already drained, then lifted the wounded man into a more comfortable place in the shade.

"Who are you, gentle one? I would know whom to thank for so much kindness to a stranger?"

But when they had disclosed each other's name and tribe, they found that their people were blood-enemies, between whom there was held a feud of many years standing. However, the call of youth toward companionship was stronger than tribal loyalty, and the young people chatted until the sun was low. Waconda rose. "I will bring you food," she said, "and when the hunters return will have my father bring you to our camp that you may be better cared for."

"No, no! I could not enter helpless into an enemy camp. My

own hunters will surely find me by nightfall."

"But you need food and care at once. You need not fear, oh, Takota. My father keeps well our tradition of hospitality, even to an enemy stranger." Waconda spoke proudly.

"I doubt it not at all, Waconda, but I could not accept it at his hands."

"You speak foolishly, young chief, but since you do not wish to heed my words I will leave you now. After sunset I will return with food."

"Do not be angry, oh Waconda, and do not trouble yourself about the food. Already I have taken from your hands far more kindness than one should accept from an enemy."

"Again you are foolish, young warrior. I am not your enemy," Waconda said smiling. "That is but our fathers' affair. I will bring you food."

She was able to carry out her plan secretly. The young brave thanked her again and again, assuring her of his undying gratitude. "My life is yours, oh Waconda of the gentle spirit. Without your kindness, it would have slipped away ere now. Whatever you ask of me, that will I do."

In the morning he was gone, but since the two hunting-camps were not a great distance apart, the young chief came into the vicinity again and again. Waconda met him often, at first by chance, then by plan, until the two had learned to love each other. One day the young chief said, "Tomorrow, oh beloved, I go to your father, to offer him many swift dogs, fine robes and other gifts, that you may come and dwell with me forever in my lodge."

"I would indeed go with you gladly, oh Takota, but I fear it is hopeless. Go, however! Perhaps the gods will be kind."

But they were not. The great chief, Waconda's father, listened courteously to the young man's suit, and sadly to his daughter's pleadings. He wished his daughter's happiness, but the tribal law against intermarriage with blood enemies was an ancient and much honored one. He could do nothing except call a council of the chiefs of both tribes, and present the case for their decision.

The council was called, but feeling ran high between these

two tribes. Angry words were spoken, faces grew dark and voices harsh with anger, so that instead of smoking the pipe of peace, a challenge of war was given and accepted. The Indians met for battle in the beautiful Solomon Valley. Back and forth the tide of struggling men surged, advancing and retreating, until at last the fight centered on the little hillock, whose age-old pool reflected alike the could-flecked blue of the sky and the fearfully-painted bodies of the warriors.

Waconda and her women stood watching not far away. Suddenly an arrow from the bow of one of her own kinsmen pierced the heart of her gallant young lover, who had been fighting daringly and bravely at the pool's edge. He caught at his breast, gave one despairing cry, and toppled backward into the blue-green water. Unheeding the flying arrows, Waconda darted to the spot. Flinging her arms aloft and calling upon the gods to give her back her lover, she plunged in after him. But the pool was deep, the jagged rocks treacherous. The green water closed over the sweethearts, and neither body was seen again.

In awe, the fighting warriors drew away and went silently to their camps. And ever afterward, in memory of this daring and heroic sacrifice, the red men called the pool Waconda, the Spring of the Great Spirit, believing that the devoted spirit of the Indian maid dwelt there with that of her lover. They worshipped there, made sacrifices of things they held most dear, and cherished the traditions of Waconda's sacred power. They believed that if they failed in doing her honor, she would cause the spring to overflow the plain, until all her people were destroyed.

Margaret Hill McCarter, who has written so many beautiful stories about Kansas, her history and her people, quotes in one of her books an old Arapahoe melody, a prayer to Waconda.

> "Waconda, hear us, hear us,
> Waconda, oh behold us,
> Like the embers dying, oh Waconda,
> Like the pale mists flying, oh Waconda,
> Fields and forests fade before us,
> Woods and streams our fathers gave us,

Home and friends of home, oh Waconda,
And thy children roam, oh Waconda,
Like the weary winds, homeless—crying."

Beautiful, is it not? These old tales and songs of a primitive people are strange indeed. One cannot trace their origin, nor tell how much may have been added from generation to generation. But this beautiful legend must lead far, far back into the very dawn of Indian religion, to the birth of the idea of sacrifice, of a Great Spirit who gave life for the sake of love.

No more do the red men worship at this prairie shrine of their Wah-kan-dah. They are gone from their ancient hunting-ground in the lovely valley of the Solomon. The sound of the war-whoop is heard no more, the cry of the chase will not again re-echo from the low-lying hills. The beat of their savage tom-toms, the plaintive minor melody of their songs, the wailing death chant is silent forever.

But on the rounded hillock raised above the level stretch of the Solomon River, serene and calm, the little pool of sea-green water still smiles into the blue Kansas sky. Age-old, and change-less through the changing years, Waconda, the Spirit of the Spring, still keeps watch.

"The Spirit of the Spring Waconda" by Jessie Kennedy Snell originally appeared in *Lore of the Great Plains*, H.F. Davis Memorial Library, Colby Community College, Colby, Kansas, 1970, pp. 95-101.

Unearthly Creatures

The Lobo Girl of Devil's River

IN THE FALL OF 1830 JOHN DENT and Will Marlo went in partners to trap fur along the headwaters of Chickamauga River in Georgia. Pelts were plentiful, and they got along harmoniously enough until the spring of 1833, when they fell out over a division of the winter's catch.

A woman was at the bottom of the quarrel. She was Mollie Pertul, daughter of a mountaineer. While trapping in the vicinity of the Pertul cabin, John Dent had fallen in love with her and the two had engaged to be married. In forming their partnership the two trappers had agreed to sell jointly all pelts they took and to divide the money equally. Through two seasons this agreement they had carried out, but now Dent insisted on taking half the hides and disposing of them in his own way. He had a notion that he could get more money, to start married life on, by selling his fur separately.

After a bitter quarrel the division was made as Dent wanted it. Immediately almost, Marlo began telling around that he had been cheated. The quarrel went on for two weeks; then there was a fight in which Dent stabbed Marlo to death. Public opinion was against him, and there was nothing for him to do but skip the country. Before leaving, however, he managed to see his love and tell her that he was going to locate a place in which they could live together and that he would return and steal her away.

Months passed by and people began to lose interest in the matter. During all this time, presumably, Mollie Pertul heard nothing from her murderer lover. Then a little after sundown on

April 13, 1834—just a year to the day after Marlo was stabbed—
the mountaineer girl went to the cow lot to milk as was her daily
custom. After she had been absent from the house an unusually
long time, her parents decided to investigate and see if anything
had gone wrong. They found the cows unmilked and in the
empty milk pail a Bowie knife with dried blood caked about the
hilt. It had a staghorn handle of peculiar design that made it
easily identified, next day, as the knife with which Dent had
killed Marlo.

In the darkness of the night the parents called and searched
for Mollie, but in vain. As soon as daylight showed, a few
mountaineers who had been summoned began looking for
sign. They struck the tracks of a man and woman leading to the
Chickamauga River. There they found in the bank a freshly
driven stob to which, apparently, a small canoe had recently
been moored. Mollie Pertul was gone without a word of explanation and without a moment's preparation. All she took with
her were the clothes on her back.

Six months passed. Then old Mrs. Pertul received a letter
postmarked Galveston, Texas. It read:

> "Dear Mother,
> "The Devil has a river in Texas that is all
>   his own and it is made only for those who are grown.
>   "Yours with love—
>   "Mollie"

In those days the people of Georgia were not familiar with
the streams of Texas and their names. Indeed, very few people
in Texas itself knew anything about Devil's River, far to the west
of San Antonio, the outpost of all settlements, its inhabitants
almost exclusively Spanish-speaking. Mrs. Pertul and her husband and neighbors merely considered that somewhere in
Texas Dent had to himself a river on which to trap. The knew
that Dent was a devil all right, though maybe they were a little
surprised at Mollie's admitting it.

Now, one of the little known chapters in Texas history is of a
small colony of English people who in 1834 settled on Devil's

River, calling their settlement Dolores. It was short-lived. Indians killed most of the settlers. A few of them drifted into Mexico. The remainder, fourteen adults and three children, in attempting to get back east were attacked at Espantosa Lake, near what is now Carrizo Springs. After killing them all, the Comanches threw their bodies and the carts in which they were traveling into the lake. That is why to this day Mexicans consider the lake haunted, the name Espantosa meaning "frightful."

Dent and his bride had joined this English colony. Devil's River had plenty of beaver; so did the Rio Grande both above and below where Devil's River empties into it. We may be sure that Dent did not live in the group of Englishmen, but, like the lone wolf he was, off to one side. He, no doubt, had an agreement with the Indians. A considerable ride westward two or three Mexican families, more Indianized than anything else, raised a few goats on the Pecos Canyon.

About noon one day in May of the year 1835, a rider on a reeling horse drew up at one of these goat ranches. He told the Mexican *ranchero* and his wife that he was camped where Dry Creek runs into Devil's River. He said that his wife was giving birth to a baby and that they must have help. The Mexican woman agreed to go with her husband, who at once began saddling the horses. Meantime, one of those black electricity-charged clouds for which that part of the country is noted was coming up. A bolt of lightning struck the messenger dead.

This delayed the Mexicans considerably in getting off. From the description of his camp site given by the dead man the ranchero knew how to reach it, but night came on before he and his wife got over the divide to Devil's River. They did not find the camp until next morning. There, under an open brush arbor lay the woman dead, alone. Indications pointed to the fact that she had died while giving birth to a child. Yet no child was visible. No child could be found. No trace of it was evident anywhere. Tracks thick around the brush arbor made the ranchero suspect that lobo wolves had devoured the infant.

In the scantily furnished brush cabin the Mexicans found a letter, which they took along to show the first person they might encounter who could read English. This letter, as it later developed, had been written by Mollie Pertul Dent to her mother in Georgia several weeks before her death. It served to identify her and her husband. Thus their romance ended.

Ten years passed. A wagon road that had been laid out across the new Republic of Texas to El Paso went by San Felipe Springs (now Del Rio), where there were a few Mexicans, and on across Devil's River, only twelve miles beyond, and then across the Pecos. Occasionally armed travelers passed over the road. In the year 1845 a boy living at San Felipe Springs reported that he had seen a pack of lobo wolves attacking a herd of goats and with them a creature, long hair half covering its features, that looked like a naked girl. Some passing Americans who heard the story quizzed him. But they seemed more interested in getting his description of what a naked girl looked like than in getting information about the strange creature he reported. The story was ridiculed, but it spread back among the settlements.

Not more than a year after this a Mexican woman at San Felipe declared she had seen two big lobos and a naked girl devouring a freshly killed goat. She got close to them, she said, before they saw her. Then they all three ran. The naked girl ran at first on all-fours, but then rose up and ran on two feet, keeping in company with the wolves. The woman was positive of what she had seen. The few people in the Devil's River country began to keep a sharp lookout for the girl. They recalled the disappearance of the dead Mollie Dent's infant amid lobo tracks. Men of the camp told how female wolves carried their cubs by the scruff of the neck without injuring them. Perhaps, they said, some lobo wolf in whom the mother instinct was strong had carried the new-born to her den and raised it. Indians reported having noted in sandy places along the river barefoot tracks, sometimes accompanied by hand prints.

A hunt was organized to capture the Lobo, or Wolf, Girl of the Devil's River, as she had now come to be called. It was made up mostly of wild-riding Mexican vaqueros. These people had doubtless never heard anything of the story of the wolf-suckled Romulus and Remus who founded Rome or of wolf-nursed children in India like Kipling's Mowgli, but far out on this isolated, stark border they had been confronted with unmistakable evidence of a human being reared by and running wild with lobo wolves.

On the third day of the hunt two of the riders jumped the girl near a side canyon. She was with a big lobo that cut off from her when she dodged into a crevice. Here the vaqueros cornered her. She cowered at first like a rabbit. Then she spat and hissed like a wildcat. She fought too, clawing and biting. While the vaqueros were tying her she began to belch forth pitiful, frightful, unearthly sounds described as resembling both the scream of a woman and the howl of a lobo but being neither. As she was howling forth this awful scream, a monster he-wolf, presumably the one from whom she had become separated, suddenly appeared rushing at her captors. The fact that one of them saw it coming before it got close enough to use its powerful jaws probably saved their lives. He shot it dead with a pistol. At that the wild girl sank into a silent faint.

The captured creature was now securely tied and could be examined more carefully. She was excessively hairy, but breasts of beautiful curvature and other features showed that she was a normally formed human female. Her hands and arms were muscled in an extraordinary manner but not ill proportioned.

Having revived from her faint, she was placed on a horse and carried to the nearest ranch. There she was unbound and turned loose in an isolated room for the night. With gestures of kindness she was offered a covering for her body, food, and water, but no eagle of the free air, no lion of the deep jungle, ever showed more distrust and fear of its captors than she. She backed into the darkest corner, and there she was left alone. The door to the room was closed. The only other opening was a little window across which a board had been nailed.

The ranch was but a two-roomed hovel, alone amid the desert wilderness. By dark four or five men were gathered at it, and now the wild and frantic being fastened up in the room began voicing forth the terrifying screamish howls. Through the log walls of many vents they carried far on the night air. Soon they were answered by the long drawn out, deep howls of lobos beyond. Lobos seemed to answer from all sides, and their dismal and far-carrying voices brought answers from farther and farther away. All the lobos of the western world seemed to be gathering. *Rancheros* who all their lives had heard lobos howl had never heard anything like this, either from such a number of wolves now assembling or in the sullen, doom-like quality of the long, deep howling. Nearer and more compactly the horde gathered. Now they would howl all in unison, a bass-throated chorus of ferocity and darkness and lost hopes such as no musician of the world ever dreamed of. Then they would be silent as if waiting for some answer, and the wild girl in the dark room there would answer back with her unearthly howling scream, a voice neither or woman nor of beast.

After a time the great pack made a rush for the corrals, attacking goats, milk cows and the saddle horses. These noises made by these domestic animals, especially the screams and neighs of the plunging, kicking horses, brought the men to the rescue. Ordinarily no man at all familiar with lobo wolves would fear one. Now these rancheros kept together, shooting in the darkness and yelling as they advanced. The wolves retreated.

Meantime, in the pandemonium, the Lobo Girl somehow wrenched the cross plank from the window and got out. It was supposed that she immediately rejoined the wolves. Hardly another howl was heard that night, and the next day not a track of the girl could be found. For a long time the sight of a wolf in that particular region was very rare.

Nothing more was heard of the Wolf Girl of Devil's River for six years. Meantime, gold had been discovered in California and travel westward had greatly increased. Along in 1852 an exploring party of frontiersmen hunting a route to El Paso that would be better watered than the Chihuahua Trail, as the road used was called, rode down to the Rio Grande at a sharp bend far above the mouth of the Devil's River.

They were almost upon the water before they saw it or could be seen from its edge. There, sitting on a sand bar, two young wolf welps tugging at her full breasts, they at close range caught clear sight of a naked young woman. In an instant she upon her feet, a whelp under each arm, dashing into the breaks at a rate no horse could follow. The creature could have been no other than the wild Lobo Girl of Devil's River.

So far as is known she was never glimpsed by man after this, though perhaps some of the old-time Apaches might have had a tale to tell could they have been asked. What the fate of the Lobo Girl—or woman—was, nobody probably will ever know. During the war of extermination that has been waged on lobos, the most predatory of animals that stockmen of America have known, in the border country, a wolf has occasionally been found with a marked human resemblance, and for many years now "human-faced" wolves, so called, have been considered the final culmination of a Georgia murder and elopement. If man can bear the "mark of the beast," why may not beast bear the mark of the man? Speaking only for myself, I will say that despite the fact that over a century has passed since the beginning of the events just related, yet during the past forty years I have in the western country met more than one wolf face strongly marked with human characteristics.

"The Lobo Girl of Devil's River" by L.D. Bertillion originally appeared in *Straight Texas*, a publication of the Texas Folk-Lore Society, Number XIII, J. Frank Dobie, editor, Southern Methodist University Press, Dallas, Texas, 1937, pp. 79-85.

Georgia's Werewolf

THE ONLY WEREWOLF IN GEORGIA'S ghostlore is said to be
buried in O'Neal's District in Talbot County. Some of the older
citizens can tell the story of the old spinster who turned into a
wolf at will to maraud among the sheep.

The whole county had always thought the oldest sister of
the Burton family was a little odd, and there was talk among the
slaves of seeing her wander among the graves in the grove
nearby or of locking herself in her room for days without seeing
anyone, but no one could put much trust in those old slave tales,
especially when they concerned such a highly respectable family as the Burtons.

It was just about the time that the Burton spinster returned
from her latest trip to Europe that the sheep of the farmers
began to be attacked. Each night, in spite of the guards around,
the marauder would take his toll—never for food, but for the joy
of killing. Several valuable sheep dogs were lost at the time, too.
Although a few of the farmers in the area reported that they had
seen the culprit and shot at it repeatedly, nothing seemed to fell
it.

Its species was unknown. There were some grey wolves still
in Georgia's forests at the time, but this animal's tracks were not
those of the grey wolf. Nor were the unearthly moans of pleasure which it sent forth after a night of killing those of any
known animal.

Traps were tried. More guards were placed over the sheep at
night. New rifles were bought and professional hunters were
engaged, but the traps remained empty. Although the hunters

seemed to hit the animal, as evidenced by a few drops of blood on the ground, the depredations continued.

One farmer who had suffered more extensive losses than the others swore that he would kill the animal. To make doubly sure that he would be rid of it, he offered a $200 reward for its head. He was surprised when he received a note asking him to go to the farm of a new settler, a man who had but recently arrived from Bohemia. The writer was a thrifty, hard-working and religious man who was separated from the people of the valley by a language barrier.

"Back home in Bohemia, I remember we have this same trouble," the immigrant said to his visitor. "People lose their sheep for months until a very smart man nearby tell us of the werewolf legend of my people. The werewolf, he love to kill for the sake of killing, just to taste the blood; not for food. So we villagers did the same thing I am asking you to do. Here is my silver cross. Take it and melt it into the shape of a bullet. Give it to your best hunter for his rifle. It is the only way a werewolf can by stopped."

Jackson, one of the victimized farmers, was desperate enough to believe anything, even a crazy tale from a foreigner. The silver cross was melted down and fitted into his own rifle, and Jackson insisted that he himself would stand guard for a few nights.

He was not kept waiting long. On the second night of his vigil the marauder came to the flock he was guarding and began its nightly slaughter. Jackson took careful aim from an advantageous position and fired. The beast screamed, but not like an animal cry. Instead it was the sound of a woman's voice— piercing, desperate, and haunting. He hurried to the place and searched closely for the animal, but it was nowhere to be found. Instead, however, he found the left front foot of the beast, where the silver bullet had cleanly sliced it off. The slaughter stopped.

No one thought it strange that the Burton spinster now had a bandaged left arm; they assumed that she must have hurt it somewhere. It was not until years later that the town doctor revealed that on the very night of the shot he had bandaged the spinster's arm for what looked like the damage from a bullet which had taken off her entire hand and wrist.

"Georgia's Werewolf" by Ronald G. Killion and Charles T. Walker originally appeared in *A Treasury of Georgia Folklore*, Cherokee Publishing Co., Atlanta, Georgia, 1972, pp. 42-44.

Witch Stump

A GROTESQUE STUMP, KNOWN as the witch stump, glares like a tiger at Dismal Swamp hunters on the west side of Lake Drummond. Uncle Johnnie Culpepper always enjoyed telling how the stump happened to be there. He said,

"A wicked old crone who lived somewhere on the west side of Dismal Swamp delighted in harassing the deer hunters' dogs. One old fellow who had been tormented by this witch for years tired of her obnoxious ways and resolved to destroy her. He worked out a deal with an Indian who was in cahoots with the devil, and took him on one of his hunts.

"When the dogs began to whine, then to yapp, the hunt started. The old witch changed herself into a doe this time and the dogs chased her. The Indian conjurer shrewdly steered the chase toward Lake Drummond. When the doe approached the water's edge the hounds began to close in on her.

"The old witch realized that the dogs would rip her to pieces, so she changed herself into a stump. Then the hunter called in his dogs and the Indian went to work. He dropped down on his knees, raised his head, lifted his arms high, cupped his hands together and began a weird chant in his native Indian langauge. Then he said, 'Diabolical master of my soul, demon of the forest, evil genius of the nether world, I have been a loyal sorcerer and have worshipped you with fervor for many years. Now I beg that one favor, please bestow upon me magic power!'

"The fiendish spirit appeared right above the Indian in a tree. He dropped a bag of green powder from the tree into the Indian's hands. The sorcerer arose, pranced about, sprinkled the green powder over the top of the stump and chanted, 'nero-c-fore, cutta-long, long-many, long-co, co-many, co-ben, ben-many, ben-cha, cha-many, wa-cheagles.'

"As the last bit of green powder fell into place over the stump eerie flames sprang up, curled high into the air, burned away all of the powers of the witch to change herself back into human form forever as a silent reminder that witches once roamed through the Dismal Swamp forests and harassed Dismal Swamp hunters.

"Lightning flashed, and a loud crack of thunder echoed through the forest. Semi-darkness enshrouded the men. A gust of fierce wind streaked through the trees as the clouds rumbled and growled and bumped together. Then a moment of frightening silence. A slow pelt of rain drops soon increased into a swish of rain which swooped down in sheets for some time. When the rain had stopped, the hunter and his Indian conjurer gathered the dogs and trudged slowly home."

"Witch Stump" by Hubert J. Davis originally appeared in *Myths and Legends of Great Dismal Swamp*, Johnson Publishing Company, Murfreesboro, North Carolina, 1981, pp. 56-58.

The Moodus Noises

THE LOWER CONNECTICUT River has many inlets and little islands near Haddam. At the place called Haddam Neck there is a hole where, according to legend, no one has ever touched bottom. Some divers believed it was an entrance to a cave which goes a great distance under the earth and river. Another great tunnel-like cave in the area has been explored only to a certain point. Beyond that point, matches, torches of fire, and even flashlights are said to go out.

Perhaps these are entrances to the underground kingdom of the Haddam witches, so famous in old tales. Many years ago, loud thunder-like crashes came from under the earth at regular intervals near Mount Tom. Mount Tom is a high hill near the point where the Moodus River and the Salmon River meet before their waters flow into the Connecticut River. Many times these fierce crashes rolling under the earth frightened the inhabitants.

The Indians had always said that these mysterious noises were caused by the Evil Spirit who was known to inhabit this region—the same Evil Spirit who jumped off Devil's Rock in Portland with the unfortunate Indian brave and who fiddled as the witches danced and worked near the falls now called Devil's Hopyard.

The early white colonists soon learned the Indian tales. The area is said to be a battleground between the Haddam witches from the west side of the Connecticut River and the East Haddam witches from the east side of the river. The Haddam witches were much feared for their evil Black Magic which causes curses, sickness, lameness, lost love—and even Death. The East Haddam witches were known for their White Magic which can cure illness, end curses, make crooked people straight, restore lost love—and even fight Death.

Far under the earth, under the hill called Mount Tom and under the Connecticut River in the great tunnel, the witches fight, curse each other, and blow up magic powders. In the caves which extend from the bottomless point in the river eastward to East Haddam and westward to Haddam, they roll huge stones and boulders toward each other—thus creating the horrible and frightening Moodus Noises.

When such battles last too long, they disturb the ruling spirit of the region, Old Machemoodus. Machemoodus is an Indian spirit who watches over the area from a sapphire throne which gleams like millions of diamonds. When he tires of the noises, he waves his precious sapphire wand and clears away the witches—both good and bad—forcing the evil ones far into the depths of the earth to the west of the river near Haddam Neck.

But then, when these evil Black Witches have gathered enough strong Black Magic, they dare to climb up slowly through the caves in great numbers and again challenge the power of the good White Witches across the river. And the scary Moodus Noises again shake Mount Tom and the country round-about it.

Even far across the ocean in England, people heard of the mysterious Moodus Noises. In the year 1765, a "Doctor" Steele from England spent much time digging and exploring the slopes of Mount Tom. He built an odd little house on the side of the mountain. To keep its secrets unknown to the nosey neighbors, he even plugged the keyhole to preserve the mysteries of the forge he worked inside the building.

One dark night, led by an eerie white light, he went to Rocky Moodus Cave and loosened the huge stone which blocked the entrance. A blood-red light is said to have shone from the cave, staining even the stars crimson. Dr. Steele vanished the next day after leaving word that he had taken away two pearls, which he said were the cause of the underground rumblings. He said, however, that other miniature pearls inside were developing and would cause future noises.

On May 16, 1791, great explosions like tremendous cannon shots were followed by two strong earth shocks which opened crevices in the earth, shattered windows, threw down chimneys and broke pipes. During that day and night, the Moodus area was shaken by more than a hundred lesser shocks, some of which were felt from New York to Boston. Eye-witnesses said that "the concussion of the earth and the roaring of the atmosphere was most tremendous" and predicted that the town of Moodus would sooner or later sink. Old-timers asked themselves whether the great earth shocks had been caused by the fighting witches or Dr. Steele's pearls.

"The Moodus Noises" originally appeared in *Folk Tales of Connecticut*, Glen E.F. White, editor, Journal Press, Meridan, Connecticut, 1977, pp. 23-25.

The Image That Came to Life

A YOUNG CHIEF ON THE QUEEN Charlotte islands married, and soon afterwards his wife fell ill. Then he sent around everywhere for the very best shamans. If there were a very fine shaman at a certain village he would send a canoe there to bring him. None of them could help her, however, and after she had been sick for a very long time she died.

Now the young chief felt very badly over the loss of his wife. He went from place to place after the best carvers in order to have them carve an image of his wife, but no one could make anything to look like her. All this time there was a carver in his own village who could carve much better than all the others. This man met him one day and said, "You are going from village to village to have wood carved like your wife's face, and you can not find anyone to do it, can you? I have seen your wife a great deal walking along with you. I have never studied her face with the idea that you might want someone to carve it, but I am going to try if you will allow me."

Then the carver went after a piece of red cedar and began working upon it. When he was through, he went to the young chief and said, "Now you can come along and look at it." He had dressed it just as he used to see the young woman dressed. So the chief went with him, and, when he got inside, he saw his dead wife sitting there just as she used to look. This made him very happy, and he took it home. Then he asked the carver, "What do I owe you for making this?" and he replied, "Do as you please about it." The carver had felt sorry to see how this chief was mourning for his wife, so he said, "It is because I felt badly for you that I made it. So don't pay me too much for it." He paid the carver very well, however, both in slaves and in goods.

Now the chief dressed this image in his wife's clothes and her marten-skin robe. He felt that his wife had come back to him and treated the image just like her. One day, while he sat mourning very close to the image, he felt it move. His wife had also been very fond of him. At first he thought that the movement was only his imagination, yet he examined it every day, for he thought that at some time it would come to life. When he ate he always had the image close to him.

After a while the whole village learned that he had this image and all came in to see it. Many could not believe that it was not the woman herself until they had examined it closely.

One day, after the chief had had it for a long, long time, he examined the body and found it just like that of a human being.

Still, although it was alive, it could not move or speak. Sometime later, however, the image gave forth a sound from its chest like that of crackling wood, and the man knew that it was ill.

When he had some one move it away from the place where it had been sitting they found a small red-cedar tree growing there on top of the flooring. They left it until it grew to be very large, and it is because of this that cedars on the Queen Charlotte islands are so good. When people up this way look for red cedars and find a good one they say, "This looks like the baby of the chief's wife."

Every day the image of the young woman grew more like a human being, and, when they heard the story, people from villages far and near came in to look at it and at the young cedar tree growing there, at which they were very much astonished. The woman moved around very little and never got to talk, but her husband dreamed what she wanted to tell him. It was through his dreams that he knew she was talking to him.

"The Image that Came to Life" by John R. Swanton originally appeared in *Tlingit Myths and Texts*, Scholarly Press, Inc., St. Clair Shores, Michigan, 1976, pp. 181-182.

Cursed Ground

The Devil's Tramping Ground

CHATHAM COUNTY, SMILINGLY known for a traditional rabbit population, also has a lively unsolved mystery—a mystery of nature.

Chatham, a historic county, was settled in 1771 by planters who moved in from the Cape Fear region. Both the county and the county seat, Pittsboro, were named for the Earl of Chatham, William Pitt, champion of colonial rights in the British Parliament.

The present Chatham County courthouse was built at Pittsboro in 1882 at a time when that village was known as Chatham Court House. Cornwallis spent a night at Chatham Court House in the course of his march to Wilmington after the Battle of Guilford Court House. David Fanning and his band of Tories once raided the town while a court-martial was in progress and captured forty-four persons as a part of Fanning's program of terrorizing that area during the Revolutionary War period. So Chatham County, rich in history, looks back over nearly two centuries of vibrant life.

Against this background we have an unsolved mystery, a curiosity of nature that has grown into a legend, has attracted thousands of visitors to the scene of the phenomenon, and has brought forth hundreds of explanations as to its origin.

We go ten miles from Siler City to a point in western Chatham County for the scene of this strange story. Here we find a cleared path, in a perfect circle, in a grove of trees on the L.R. Down property. This path has existed as far back as the memory of man—and it has always been just as it is found today, without

74

so much as a sprig of vegetation growing in the pathway. The spot is just off a rural highway and has no more official marking or designation than a state highway sign at Harper Cross Roads, one mile distant, pointing to the odd spot.

It's the Devil's Tramping Ground, the Chatham natives say. And the story is that the Devil goes there to walk in circles as he thinks up new means of causing trouble for humanity. There, sometime during the dark of night, the Majesty of the Underworld of Evil silently tramps around and around that bare circle—thinking, plotting, and planning against good, and in behalf of wrong.

So far as is known, no person has ever spent the night there to disprove that this is what happens and that this is what keeps grass, weeds, and other vegetation worn clean and bare from the circle called the Devil's Tramping Ground.

The cleared spot, surrounded by trees, comprises a perfect circle with a forty-foot diameter. The path itself is about a foot wide and is barren of any obstruction—growing or otherwise. A certain variety of wire grass grows inside the circle in a limited fashion and residents of that neighborhood say that any attempts to transplant any of it have met with failure. Broomsedge, moss, and grasses grow on the outer edge of the circular path, but not inside the circle.

Persons who visit the spot frequently place sticks and stones in the path and sometimes tie sticks there, anchoring them with strings across the cleared band of earth, but the path is always found clear the next day. This, the story has it, indicates that the Devil kicks the obstacles aside on his nightly perambulations.

Many have been the explanations offered for this oddity of nature—this perfect circle that year after year ever remains clear of any growth whatsoever.

One of the oldest and best-known of the legendary explanations for the Devil's Tramping Ground is that hundreds of years ago when many Indian tribes roamed the section that is now Chatham County—known then to the Indians as the Great Flats—the tribes would meet at periodic occasions in celebrations and feasts. The spot that is today known as the Devil's Tramping Ground was a principal meeting place for these occa-

75

sions of festivity, assembly, and counciling.

Thousands of these first Americans would gather and the braves would hold their vigorous war dances. The treading of their feet wore a circle in the earth as the Indians called on The Great Spirit in the Happy Hunting Ground to give them success in their enterprises of war. And their God has kept, as a token and a monument to these faithful Indian braves, that circle that their moccasined feet wore bare as they danced about their camp fire in supplication to him and in defiance of their enemies.

And there is another Indian legend about the spot, and this one ties in with the Lost Colony of Roanoke Island—as do many Tar Heel Indian legends.

Years before the first white settlers came to this region, two rival Indian tribes met in battle at the present scene of the Devil's Tramping Ground and after a short but bitter conflict stained the ground thereabouts with the blood of the dead and wounded. The leader of one of the tribes was named Chief Croatan and he was killed in the engagement. With the leader of this tribe gone and casualties severe, the remaining warriors gathered the women and children of the tribe together, and with brief but impressive ceremony buried their chief in a spot that is today the exact center of the Devil's Tramping Ground. They named the spot Croatan in honor of their fallen chief and then fled eastward to the North Carolina coast to avoid further contact with their superior enemy and to start the life of their weakened tribe anew in another place.

This particular legend contends further that it was this spot—named Croatan after the dead Chief Croatan—that the members of the Lost Colony were headed for when they carved the word "Croatoan" on a tree and left the site of Sir Walter Raleigh's colony on Roanoke Island, to be forever swallowed up in oblivion.

And, according to this second Indian story, since Chief Croatan was buried there, the Great Spirit has kept bare the circle around the grave, down through the years, in mourning for the loss of a faithful chief and a great leader.

There are still other explanations to be had in the western

Chatham countryside. Natives there will tell you that the bare and circular path was made of the hoofs of many horses and mules as they circled to supply the power for grinding cane at a one-time molasses mill—and that the tread was so pronounced that vegetation has never returned. Other paths made at other treadmills pulled by horses have not, however, borne out this theory.

Legend further has it that no birds build their nests in trees adjacent to this spot and that wild game is never found there. Lawyer L.P. Dixon of Siler City tells of a certain possum-hunting incident. When the hunting party approached the Devil's Tramping Ground, he says, the dogs lowered their tails, gave up the warm trail they were following, and dropped in behind their masters to have the safety and protection of human beings.

Years ago travellers never dared to pass the spot after night-fall.

Perhaps the best explanation, and certainly the most scientific approach to a solution of the mystery came first from Harry Davis, curator of the North Carolina State Museum. Curator Davis was in that area on one occasion, with Dr. J.L. Stuckey, state geologist, when they were testing wells for their sodium chloride content—and sodium chloride is commom salt.

While in the vicinity they encountered the remains of ancient salt licks that had been used by buffalo and deer—and buffalo and deer did roam the Chatham terrain in days long gone. In the area, Mr. Davis noted several instances of vegetation that thrives on moisture from brackish water such as is found along the coast. There is other definite evidence of a pretty heavy salt content in some parts of that section.

Mr. Davis thinks that the Devil's Tramping Ground is nothing more or less than a spot of earth that is sufficiently loaded with salt to prevent ordinary vegetation from thriving there.

And this horse-back opinion of the curator of the Raleigh Museum has been backed up by recent scientific investigations. But even these investigations did not solve the mystery.

W.A. Bridges, of the W.A. Bridges Laboratory at Wilson, and Dr. I.E. Miles, director of the Soil Testing Division of the North Carolina Department of Agriculture, ran tests on samples of soil taken from the middle of the circular path. I made arrangements for the samples of soil to be taken by W.B. Morgan, Siler City newspaper man, after a Devil's Tramping Ground radio program that I presented had produced such a widespread interest over the state.

The tests by both chemists showed that the soil in the path of the Devil's Tramping Ground is sterile. Mr. Bridge's report said in part: "Although there may be other factors of a physical nature that would make this a sterile soil, our findings show that plant life will not be supported on a soil that is so acid and so low in the necessary soil nutriments."

But the mystery that remains in the face of that scientific finding presents the questions: With the soil in this curious spot too poor to support plant life, why the circular path with grass and trees growing right up to its edge? Soil rebuilds itself over a period of time; so why has this spot remained unfruitful as far back as we have recorded history, as far back as the Indian age and even to the time two hundred years ago when settlers first came into this territory? So science deepens our mystery as it seeks to solve it.

Meantime, the natives of western Chatham and many of the thousands of people who go there to examine the curious spot adhere strongly to the belief that the Devil himself has reserved that spot of land for his personal use.

I heard a story from Dr. Will Long of Graham which bears out Harry Davis' contention that the explanation of the Devil's Tramping Ground lies in a salt content of the earth there. Dr. Long told me of a strange sight seen in Chatham County in his youth. Passing a certain area there one day, he saw sheep come pouring up out of the ground in a long chain of scurrying animals—an amazing sight indeed!

Investigation revealed that the sheep were down in an old salt lick of the sort that Mr. Davis said was used in others ages by buffalo and deer, back when the Indians knew the area as the Great Flats. Animals—wild and domestic—that had roamed those hillsides for years had licked at the salt deposit and eaten it away until a great cave had been carved out in the earth. The sheep of Dr. Long's story, like many an animal before them, had gone into the opening for a few licks at the salty formation there.

There are two man-made scars at the Devil's Tramping Ground. They are holes in the center of the Tramping Ground and they were made there by unknown vandals and treasure seekers who dug there as a result of still another legend that has grown up about the place—indicating that there is a buried treasure under the eerie spot. There is no available explanation as to the source of this theory about hidden wealth.

Just who first discovered the spot is not known. There is evidence that the story of the Devil and his nightly meditative walks have been handed along for more than 150 years, from one generation of residents in that section to another.

There is no evidence that the Devil—if he still goes tramp-tramping there in a circle in the dark of night—has ever resented the curiosity that has brought thousands to his tramping ground for a possible invasion of his privacy. But if he takes his nightly walks in Chatham, and if he thinks as he tramps, and if this thinking is as evil as one would suppose, then many of the world's woes have been generated in lovely, rural Chatham County.

"The Devil's Tramping Ground" by John Harden originally appeared in *The Devil's Tramping Ground and Other North Carolina Mystery Stories*, The University of North Carolina Press, Chapel Hill, North Carolina, 1949, pp. 53-60.

Jacksonboro: The Town That Died of a Curse

IN THE FALL OF 1830 LORENZO Dow was travelling about the hamlets of Georgia looking for sinful folks who needed to be saved by his preaching. He should have been quite happy with the little town of Jacksonboro, for it had the reputation of being the roughest town on the Georgia frontier. Located near Sylvania, one hundred miles upriver from Savannah, it was a pioneer settlement hewn out of the Georgia pine wilderness. The brawny lumbermen of the area made their living by felling the great pines, nailing them together into crude rafts, and then poling the clumsy flatboats down the swift, winding Savannah to a market greedy for the hard-to-harvest crop.

When the men returned they were ready for what they termed a little entertainment, which usually started with a visit to Nell's Saloon (or maybe the White Elk, which was next door) and ended with a street fight. A Georgia historian of 1829 says that "...in the morning after the drunken frolics and fights, you could see children picking up eyeballs in tea saucers! There was so much gouging going on!" Of course some people doubt historians, but that's just what he said.

It was regrettable that Evangelist Dow entered town just as the men were celebrating the naming of their hamlet as the county seat. Dow was a strange sight with his long black hair streaming down his back, his wild eyes that shown brighter when he screamed at the top of his lungs to the drunken revellers, "Repent, brothers, repent!"

The men were in no mood for repenting at the moment. I suppose Dow didn't really know that, or perhaps he'd have waited till another time to visit. You have to give him credit for perserverance, however, for the little hunch-back preacher wasn't satisfied with just telling the men to repent; he insisted on overturning drinks and pushing the inebriates out of the saloon into the streets to hear him. No wonder that when he rounded up enough people for a congregation, he received a barrage of rotten eggs and tomatoes instead of the strains of "In the Sweet Bye and Bye."

Finally, the men could take no more of his preaching, and several went for a rope to hang the screaming little evangelist. "String him up, and let's get back to the saloon," yelled Big Nell. She was echoed by persons expressing similar sentiments. They grabbed the little preacher and already had the rope around his neck when a shout of "Stop that!" was heard.

They stopped, because the man who shouted owned most of the land nearby. His name was Goodall, and while he had no particular interest in the wild preacher or his message, he did care for law. The rope was taken from Dow's neck and Goodall asked him to remain the night at his house on the edge of town where he would be safe. Besides, he felt a little sorry for the man. He had heard rumors from Massachusetts, where the little Methodist minister had started his ministry, that he intended to convert every sinner in every frontier village on the Eastern seaboard.

Now the first part is in doubt, but Dow's preaching did take him a long way—from Massachusetts to Western New York and Ohio, back to Virginia, through the Carolinas and down to Georgia, where he insisted he found the wickedest folk of all. Some said the little man was just plain crazy, but he had his followers, too. He had no money of his own, living entirely on the charity of those to whom he preached, depending upon them for the small amount of food, clothing and shelter he required. Sometimes he was forced to sell his horse, but then he'd walk for miles with his feet bound in rags until someone provided him with another animal.

He met a variety of receptions. On occasion he had been run

out of town. In Charleston he was jailed for twenty-four hours and fined. In Savannah he preached on three occasions to vast crowds. However, never had he found men so sinful nor less ready to repent of their sins than in Jacksonboro.

The morning after his unexpected reprieve he returned to town and gathered a crowd around him. "I hate to do this to you people, but it's been commanded," he shouted. "Since you wouldn't receive me I plan to shake the dust off my feet as I leave your town. The place will die, and with it, I hope some of your wickedness."

Laughter came from a few hecklers and soon spread among the crowd. The audience bent double with guffaws. Imagine that little runt cursing the promising town of Jacksonboro!

"Except for the Goodall home, of course," Dow corrected. "There I was received." And the little preacher got on his horse, rode to the edge of town, and as he shook his feet free of the dust of the village, he pronounced the curse of Sodom on its inhabitants. No one thought anything odd when the first home burned that very night. After all, there were fires all the time. On the second day there was a small landslide on the mountain nearby, and this time two houses were completely covered by rocks and several villagers were killed.

This was only the beginning of the tragedies. During the next two years houses were destroyed by unexplained fires, damaged by mysterious winds which ripped off roofs, and battered by flash floods from the usually quiet creek. The market for pine dropped in Savannah, and the Legislature ordered that the county seat be moved to another town.

No one ever said it aloud, but they all knew. "Repent, repent," they kept hearing when the wind was strongest, and some unexplainable and seemingly supernatural event would occur, taking with it another of the structures of the place. Soon the remaining families began leaving, too. But the curse did not stop the rampaging accidents and by 1840 the town of Jacksonboro no longer existed.

Except for one house. If all these natural phenomena were merely the result of nature, they why does the Goodall home still stand? But there it is, even today. Not so beautiful as it used to be, but it is still there.

A visitor can look for miles around, however, and he won't find a nail or a board of what was once the thriving little village of Jacksonboro. Walk every foot of it, and there's not one other stick, stone, smidgen of glass to offer that anything was there. Just natural progress, the younger people say, but most of the old folk nod their heads and still believe that Jacksonboro vanished because of the curse of Lorenzo Dow.

"Jacksonboro: the Town that Died of a Curse" by Ronald G. Killion and Charles T. Walker originally appeared in *A Treasury of Georgia Folklore*, Cherokee Publishing Co., Atlanta, Georgia, 1972, pp. 50-52.

The Girl Who Was Scared to Death

(Collected from Mrs. Ivan Westerhaus, of Marion, Kansas, by Bettie Nebergall, her daughter, 7 July 1958. Mrs. Westerhaus learned this story from her mother, Mrs. Katherine Breidenstein, who was born in Lauderbach, Germany.)

SEVERAL YOUNG PEOPLE WERE at a party and were eager to find something different to do. Someone offered the dare that no one would volunteer to go to a cemetery and drive a stick into a grave. After a long silence, one young girl said she would go and would return in a very short time. She went to the grave, plunged the stick into the grave and turned away. In the dark she had driven the stick through her long skirt. When she turned to run she could not move. Horrified that death's hand had reached out from the grave to stop her, she collapsed and died. Her friends found her still pinned to the grave.

"The Girl Who Was Scared to Death" by S.J. Sackett and William E. Koch originally appeared in *Kansas Folklore*, University of Nebraska Press, Lincoln, Nebraska, 1961, p. 35.

Lost Cave With the Iron Door

DEEP IN THE RUGGEDEST PART of the boulder-jumbled Wichitas men have sought a fabulous lost mine and its treasure for the better part of three-quarters of a century. Second in popularity only to the two million dollar Jesse James treasure, the legendary Lost Cave With the Iron Door has drawn treasure seekers from both far and near.

The cave is reputed to hold eleven million dollars in Spanish gold. The treasure consists of gold ingots stacked like cordwood and baskets filled with gold doubloons—all guarded by a heavy door of iron, a massive chain, and a huge lock—not to mention the skeletons of seventeen Indians who watch over the golden treasure. The rust-eaten iron door was closed more than two hundred years ago, and no one has opened it since—except perhaps one party who glimpsed its contents for a brief moment.

That is only one version of this strange story, for some say that it contains two hundred thousand dollars of the Jesse James loot, while others believe that the cave holds five hundred thousand dollars of Belle Starr's booty. And then there is the story of a seventy-year-old woman named Holt who came to the Wichitas from Missouri in 1908. She brought with her a large iron key and a map to the cave and claimed that a dying outlaw had revealed to her its whereabouts.

Still another tradition says that the Cave with the Iron Door was not only a storage vault for gold but also a prison for Indian slaves working Spanish mines in these mountains during the eighteenth century. When Indians drove the Spaniards from the hills, they closed their mines, and pounded an iron spike into an oak tree nearby to mark their return route if that day came.

To support this story, there are those who will point out that some years ago such an iron spike was found deeply embedded in an ancient oak that had been cut down near Treasure Lake in the Wichita Mountains Wildlife Refuge, the very area in which the Iron Door has most often been seen, for on more than one occasion it has been found. Even though conflicting stories are told about the mysterious cave, they only stir the enthusiasm to find it.

One treasure hunter who believes the legend of Spanish gold—and that it will be found in an underground, concrete-)like vault—is Dave Hungerford, of Faxon, southwest of Lawton. One summer afternoon Hungerford told me about a Mexican who had inherited a curious map showing more than one hidden Spanish cache in the Wichitas, deposited for safe-keeping during the days of the Spaniards' mining operations. The map, made of fine silk, was about five feet long and two feet wide. Each of the treasure sites appeared in its own beautiful design and color. The Mexican always wore the prized cloth around his waist, inside his clothes, knowing no one would ever take his guarded possession unless that person killed him first.

The Mexican had once tried to find the huge underground gold storage. He failed, although he claimed to have found some of the smaller caches. Finally one day he permitted a friend to copy the silk map on paper but warned him that he would only be wasting his time to look for the hidden vault, for all attempts to find it had failed.

The names of those involved in this story have long been lost. But that an expedition was led into the Wichita Mountains some time in the 1850's is a story believed as fact by Hunger-ford, for he heard the story from one who had seen the copied map and knew its history. Despite the Mexican's warning the seekers actually found the cave. After much difficulty they found the ground under which the ancient vault was mapped to lie, hidden several feet below the surface. The leader instructed his men to dig. Several feet into the earth one workman struck the side of a rock wall. Frantically he swung his pick against the stone barrier, eventually working a small passage into the dark, musty tomb.

He lit a torch. What he witnessed was unreal—treasure beyond his wildest dreams. More of the men climbed down into the dark pit to cast their eyes on the unbelievable discovery. Gold bars were stacked against the walls like cordwood. Baskets on the floor overflowed with gold coins glittering in the light of the torch. In one corner of the dark room sprawled human skeletons. The intruders were not given time enough to count the grisly creatures.

Before they had had a chance to examine their new-found wealth, a sentinal on top yelled "Indians, Indians!" The cloud of dust rising from their tracks revealed that they were many in number. In terror the men clambered out of the hole, jumped on their horses, and galloped for shelter.

Most of the day passed before the fortune hunters crept back to the treasure hole, only to find to their dismay that it had been entirely filled in. So the Indians knew about it, too. They could not risk the excavation again. The next time they might not be so lucky. The bones they had seen in the treasure vault were sufficient. After marking the place well, the adventurers rode south. Added troubles and the Civil War prevented a further attempt to retrieve the treasure, but their story lives on vividly in the mind of Dave Hungerford, who has spent many a day seeking the lost treasure vault.

Others have happened upon the ancient iron door when least expecting to. Some time in the early 1900's an old man and his son were riding their horses from the Wildlife Refuge headquarters to Indiahoma, a small settlement south of the mountains. It was already late in the afternoon, and in order to reach the home of friends before dark, they took a short cut through the hills near Elk Mountain instead of riding the long road around.

While traveling through a remote canyon, a rust-worn door set into the face of a cliff caught their attention. Perhaps it was the right time of day, the right reflection, that attracted their eyes to the metal door. Or perhaps it was only a mirage. But it was strange. Because they wanted to reach their destination before nightfall, they rode on. But for the rest of their journey they discussed the discovery found so far from the nearest road.

When they arrived at the home of their friends, the father told about seeing the mysterious door and asked if anything was known about it. Their host reacted excitedly. Yes, he said, he had heard of such a cave that had been sought for many years. As their lanterns burned long into the night, they made plans to return to the cave the next day.

The search party got underway early the next morning. The old man and his son were positive that they would have no trouble retracing their tracks to the canyon where they had seen the door. But once they were in the maze of canyons, carpeted with scrub oak and cedar, father and son disagreed on the route they had taken. One canyon now looked like another.

After talking it over, the men rode up a familiar trail and then another. Nothing was found. They returned to a junction and took still another trail through the mountains. Again the route proved unfruitful. Unable to find the lost canyon, the party spread out, spending the remainder of the day combing the rugged mountain terrain.

That night the father and son returned home, still trying to recall through which the maze of canyons they had ridden. The following morning they started their search anew from the refuge headquarters. But again the trail revealed nothing. It was almost as if the canyon had been swallowed up, taking the legendary door with it. Afterward the old man and his son camped in the mountains spending weeks at a time combing the mountain wilderness. But always their painstaking attempts were futile. They never forgot what their eyes had seen. Whatever it was, they were sure that it was no mirage.

The father and son were not the last to stumble onto the disappearing portal. About 1910 a boy named Prince happened to be at the right place at the right time. Accompanying him were a girl and another couple who all plainly saw the door and its large, rusted padlock. Prince knew nothing about the cave then, but the picture of that massive metal door remained vividly in his mind. Years afterward he heard stories about the cave and hunted it many times with his brother, who today lives in Indiahoma. They, too, failed to refind it and Prince believed that only a landslide could have concealed it. He recalled that he had come upon the iron door while walking in a canyon somewhere north of Treasure Lake—the same area in which the old man and his son had glimpsed the strange door.

The grand old prospector of the Wichitas remembered still other seekers of the hidden cave. Silas Lee Ison hunted the door for more than seventy years, and was sure that someone would someday find it.

"I've worn out a good many pairs of shoes lookin' for that darn door!" said Silas emphatically, as I sat in his rustic cobblestone cabin at the foot of rugged granite peaks. "About 1908," he went on, dumping the ashes from his pipe, "a woman named Holt showed up at our camp. She was seventy years old I guess, and told us she had come from Missouri."

The woman, who had brought with her a crude map, asked for help in finding certain landmarks in the mountains, Silas said. Later she admitted that she was seeking the iron door. For almost a month, while a guest at the Ison home, she combed the country for clues, assisted by Silas' father, who had met Jesse and Frank James there in 1867. Mrs. Holt had also brought a large iron key with her, which, for reasons known only to herself, she was sure would fit the huge lock to the iron door. But even her map led her no closer to the treasure. All attempts at finding the mysterious door ended as always before.

When Mrs. Holt finally left the country, she took the map and the strange-looking key with her. What she knew she managed to keep a secret, divulging nothing more than was absolutely necessary.

With a twinkle in his eye (and a yen to take another look himself) Silas recalled another occasion on which he believed the lost door was found. About thirty years ago—perhaps more—some men were hunting raccoons one evening on the western side of the mountains. When their dogs treed one of the animals, a hunter was attracted to something in the distance that seemed to reflect the sun sinking behind the mountains. He climbed around a huge boulder to have a better look.

The eye-catching object turned out to be a massive hunk of

iron set into the face of a cliff. It was dusk, and the hunters had no time to investigate. When they returned at their earliest opportunity some days later in hopes of discovering the cave's wealth, they could not find the door.

Another version of this tale claims that the notorious outlaw Belle Starr and her associates waylaid a train from which they took half a million dollars in United States government gold and silver. The gang had already picked a cavern for the loot but needed a cover for the hideout. The door of the baggage car seemed fitting. Both the money and the steel-bound door were hauled to the cavern in the Wichitas, where Belle had been storing supplies and accumulated spoils.

The door was set in place so that it could be swung open and closed and locked. Brush, trees, and stones were placed so that the door was impossible to detect unless one was directly in front of it. Some time later the members of Belle's gang were killed. On February 2, 1889, the bandit queen was murdered in eastern Oklahoma by a killer whose identity has never been established for certain.

Others have found the lost door. A man named Stephens reported that he found it while hiking in the mountains. He tried to break it down and then climbed to the top of the mountains on which the door was fixed and there piled stones to serve as a marker. When he returned to the mountains with his brothers, he failed to find the mountain or his cairn.

In the late 1920's three boys were traveling on foot from Cooperton, northwest of the Wichitas, to Indiahoma. One of those boys was John French, of Lawton. When nightfall was near, the boys cut across country to save time. French told me that before they entered Cutthroat Gap they found an old rock pen that looked as though it had not been occupied for years. From it they traveled south and soon afterward found an oak tree from which hung an old rifle, which they cut down and took with them.

When they neared Mount Pinchot, their path took them past a rusty door that appeared to have been mounted over a cave or mine. The ironbound door was fastened with hinges and a large padlock and was so thoroughly secured that they made no attempt to open it.

An old Indian later told French that behind the iron door was a great treasure and that the spirits of dead ones inside guarded it. The aged warrior believed that he knew the location of the cave but said that tribal laws forbade him to show it to any white man. The Indian chief died keeping his tribal secret.

John French has never forgotten the strange door he chanced upon fifty years ago, but all his searches for it ended as before. Nearly all who have found the door have placed it in the mountainous terrain north of Treasure Lake, near Elk Mountain. French and his party, however, believed that they found it several miles farther north, near Mount Pinchot.

One summer during the depression of the 1930's a farm worker decided to hike to Lawton from his home in Hobart. After traveling all day, he set up camp at dusk. The next day his route took him through the mountains past Elk Mountain. As he walked, he saw the rust-stained door, barely exposed on the face of the mountainside. He had heard the iron-door legend, and he was determined not to leave without a look inside. For most of the day he tried to open the door, banging and prying at it with rocks and tree limbs. But it had been sealed far too long. The corroded metal would take modern tools to pry it from its hinges. He walked on to Indiahoma to solicit help in opening the cave.

In town two men furnished picks, hammers, and dynamite. The trio hurried back to the hills and hiked to Elk Mountain, determined to find the riches or prove the legend a hoax once and for all.

The worker and his partners climbed Elk Mountain. They spent much of the day scanning the nearby peaks from the top of the mountain, but nowhere was the door to be seen. The laborer had been positive that he could walk directly to it again. For days the men combed the boulder strewn land—some of the most rugged parts of the Wichitas—but, like all the others who had discovered the door, they were unable to find it later on.

And as late as June, 1967, I received a telephone call from an Oklahoma City resident who claimed to have glimpsed the iron door while riding horseback not far north of Treasure Lake.

When he returned on foot, no door was to be seen.

How long will the door, rusting among the red-granite rocks, hide from those who would dare to reveal its secrets? When again will it reveal itself, always to the ill-prepared traveler who least expects to stumble across it?

"Lost Cave With the Iron Door" by Steve Wilson originally appeared in *Oklahoma Treasures and Treasure Tales*, University of Oklahoma Press, Norman, Oklahoma, 1976, pp. 209-213. © 1976 by the University of Oklahoma Press.

Spirits Walk

The Ghostly Usher of Minneapolis

FOR THIS ACCOUNT, I AM INDEBTED to a twenty-two-year-old creative production assistant in a Minneapolis advertising agency by the name of Deborah Turner. Miss Turner got hooked on some of my books and started to look around in the Twin Cities for cases that might whet my appetite for ghost hunting. Being also musically inclined with an interest in theater, it was natural that she should gravitate toward the famed Guthrie Theater, named after the famous director, which is justly known as the pride of Minneapolis. At the theater she met some other young people, also in their early twenties, and shared her interest in psychic phenomena with them. Imagine her surprise when she discovered that she had stumbled upon a most interesting case.

Richard Miller was born in Manhattan, Kansas, in 1951. Until age ten, he lived there with his father, a chemist in government service. Then his father was transferred to England, and Richard spent several years going to school in that country. After that, he and his family returned to the United States and moved to Edina. This left Richard not only with a vivid recollection of England, but also somewhat of an accent which, together with his childhood in Kansas, gave him a somewhat unusual personality. His strange accent became the subject of ridicule by other students at Edina Morningside High School where he went to school and it did not go down well with the shy, introspective young man. In the tenth grade at his school, he made friends with another young man, Fred Koivumaki, and a good and close relationship sprang up between the

94

two boys. It gave Fred a chance to get to know Richard better than most of the other fellows in school.

As if the strange accent were not enough to make him stand out from the other boys in the area, Richard was given to sudden, jerky movements, which made him a good target for sly remarks and jokes of his fellow students. The Millers did not have much of a social life, since they did not quite fit into the pattern of life in the small town of Edina.

During the years spent in an English school, Richard had known corporal punishment, since it is still part of the system in some English schools. This terrified him, and perhaps contributed towards his inability to express himself fully and freely. Somehow he never aquired a girlfriend as the other students did, and this, too, bothered him a lot. He couldn't for the world understand why people didn't like him more, and often talked about it to his friend Fred.

When both young men reached the age of sixteen, they went to the Guthrie Theater where they got jobs as ushers. They worked at it for two years. Richard Miller got along well with the other ushers, but developed a close friendship only with Fred and another fellow, Barry Peterson. It is perhaps a strange quirk of fate that both Richard Miller and Barry Peterson never reached manhood, but died violently long before their time.

However, Richard's parents decided he should go to the university, and quit his job. In order to oblige his parents, Richard Miller gave up the job as usher and moved into Territorial Hall for his first year at the university.

However, the change did not increase his ability to express himself or to have a good social life. Also, he seemed to have felt that he was catering to his parents' wishes, and became more antagonistic toward them. Then, too, it appears that these students also made him the butt of their jokes. Coincidentally, he developed a vision problem, with cells breaking off his retinas and floating in the inner humor of the eye. This caused him to see spots before his eyes, a condition for which there is no cure. However, he enjoyed skiing because he knew how to do it well, and joined the university ski club.

But Richard's bad luck somehow was still with him. On a

trip to Colorado, he ran into a tree, luckily breaking only his skis. When summer came to the area, Richard rode his bike down a large dirt hill into rough ground and tall weeds at the bottom, injuring himself in the process. Fortunately, a motorcyclist came by just then, and got Richard to the emergency ward of a nearby hospital. All this may have contributed towards an ultimate breakdown; or, as the students would call it, Richard just "flipped out."

He was hospitalized at the university hospital and was allowed home only on weekends. During that time he was on strong medication, but when the medication did not improve his condition, the doctor took him off it and sent him home.

The following February 4, he decided to try skiing again, and asked his father to take him out to Buck Hill, one of the skiing areas not far from town. But to his dismay Richard discovered that he couldn't ski anymore, and this really depressed him. When he got home, there was a form letter waiting for him from the university, advising him that because he had skipped all the final exams due to his emotional problems at the time, he had received F's in all his classes and was on probation.

All this seemed too much for him. He asked his mother for forty dollars, ostensibly to buy himself new ski boots. Then he drove down to Sears on Lake Street, where he bought a high-powered pistol and shells. That was on Saturday, and he killed himself in the car. He wasn't found until Monday morning, when the lot clearing crew found him with most of his head shot off.

Richard Miller was given a quiet burial in Fort Snelling National Cemetery. His parents, Dr. and Mrs. Byron S. Miller, requested that memorials to the Minnesota Association for Mental Health be sent instead of flowers. Richard's mother had always felt that her son's best years had been spent as an usher at the Guthrie Theater; consequently he was cremated wearing his Guthrie Theater blazer. The date was February 7, and soon enough the shock of the young man's untimely death wore off, and only his immediate family and the few friends he had made remembered Richard Miller.

A few weeks after the death of the young usher, a woman seated in the theater in an aisle seat came up to the usher in charge of this aisle and asked him to stop the other usher from walking up and down during the play. The usher in charge was shocked, since he had been at the top of the aisle and had seen no one walk up and down. All the other ushers were busy in their respective aisles. However, the lady insisted that she had seen this young man walk up and down the aisle during the play. The usher in charge asked her to describe what she had seen. She described Richard Miller, even to the mole on his cheek. The incident is on record with the Guthrie Theater. Minneapolis Tribune columnist Robert T. Smith interviewed Craig Scherfenberg, director of audience development at the theater, concerning the incident. "There was no one in our employ at the time who fit the description," the director said, "but it fit the dead young man perfectly."

In the summer several years later, two ushers were asked to spend the night in the theater to make sure some troublesome air conditioning equipment was fully repaired. The Guthrie Theater has a thrust stage with openings onto the stage on all three sides; these openings lead to an actors' waiting area, which in turn has a door opening onto an area used as a lounge during intermissions.

The two young men were sitting in this waiting area with both doors open, and they were the only people in the building. At one o'clock in the morning, they suddenly heard the piano onstage begin to play. Stunned by this, they watched in silence when they saw a cloud-like form floating through the lounge door and hovering in the center of the room. One of the ushers thought the form was staring at him. As quickly as they could gather their wits they left the room.

One of Deborah Turner's friends had worked late one evening shortly after this incident, repairing costumes needed for the next day's performance. She and a friend were relaxing in the stage area while waiting for a ride home. As she glanced into the house, she noticed that the lights on the aisle that had been the dead usher's were going on and off, as if someone were walking slowly up and down. She went to the ladies' room a little later, and suddenly she heard pounding on one wall, eventually circling the room and causing her great anxiety, since she knew that she and her friend were the only people in the house.

When the Guthrie Theater put on a performance of *Julius Caesar*, one of the extras was an older woman by the name of Mary Parez. She freely admitted that she was psychic and had been able to communicate with her dead sister. She told her fellow actors that she could sense Richard Miller's presence in the auditorium. Somehow she thought that the ghost would make himself known during Mark Antony's famous speech to the Romans after Caesar's death.

The scene was lit primarily by torches when the body of Julius Caesar was brought upon the stage. Jason Harlen, a young usher, and one of his colleagues were watching the performance from different vantage points in the theater. One boy was in one of the tunnels leading to the stage, the other in the audience. Both had been told of Mary Parez's prediction, but were disappointed when nothing happened at that time. In boredom, they began to look around the theater. Independently of each other, they saw smoke rising to the ceiling, and shaping itself into a human form. Both young men said that the form had human eyes.

The aisle that the late Richard Miller worked was number eighteen. Two women in the acting company of *Julius Caesar*, named Terry and Gigi, complained that they had much trouble with the door at the top of aisle eighteen for no apparent reason. Bruce Benson, who now worked aisle eighteen, told that people complained of an usher walking up and down the aisle during performances. Bruce Margolis, who works the stage door, leaves the building after everyone else. When he was there one night all alone, the elevator began running on its own.

All this talk about a ghost induced some of the young ushers to try and make contact with him via the Ouija board. Dan Berry, head usher, took a board with him to the stage, and along with colleagues Bruce Benson and Scott Hurner, tried to communicate with the ghost. For awhile nothing happened. Then, all of a sudden, the board spelled "Tiptoe to the tech room."

When they asked why, the board spelled the word ghost. They wanted to know which tech room the ghost was referring to: downstairs? "No," the communicator informed them, "upstairs." Then the board signed off with the initials MIL. At that, one of the men tipped over the board and wanted nothing further to do with it.

In November of the next year, an usher working at the theater told columnist Robert Smith, "It was after a night performance. Everyone had left the theater but me. I had forgotten my gloves and returned to retrieve them. I glanced into the theater and saw an usher standing in one of the aisles. It was him. He saw me and left. I went around to the aisle and couldn't find anything."

There is also an opera company connected with the Guthrie Theater. One night not long ago, one of the ladies working for the opera company was driving home from the Guthrie Theater. Suddenly she felt a presence beside her in the car. Terrified, she looked around, and became aware of a young man with dark curly hair, glasses, and a mole on his face. He wore a blue coat with something red on the pocket—the Guthrie Theater blazer. With a sinking feeling, she realized that she was looking at the ghost of Richard Miller.

For the past two years, however, no new reports have come in concerning the unfortunate young man. Could it be that he has finally realized that there await him greater opportunities in the next dimension, and though his life on earth was not very successful, his passing into the spiritual life might give him most of the opportunities his life on earth had denied him? At any rate, things have now quieted down in aisle eighteen at the Guthrie Theater, in Minneapolis, Minnesota.

"The Ghostly Usher of Minneapolis" by Hans Holzer orginally appeared in the book, *Best True Ghost Stories*, copyright 1983, pp. 141-145. Used by pemission of the publisher, Prentice-Hall, Inc., Englewood Cliffs, New Jersey.

The Blond on the Skyway Bridge: Real or Fantasy?

BEFORE THE SKYWAY BRIDGE fell, the young woman spent most of her time at the top of the superstructure, where the asphalt roadway arched into a few hundred feet of steel grating. There, where the deep hum of traffic segues into a chilling metallic roar, she would stand oblivious to fright.

It's scary and mysterious on the apex of that bridge. But the blond didn't seem to care. Either she insolently glared at coming traffic with arms akimbo, or she placed her hands against the girders and looked out to the dizzy water below. Her hair was always blowing wildly. White-blond and windblown.

And then, suddenly, she would be gone.

Back, perhaps, the next dark and lonely night.

No one has been found who stopped and actually talked to her in those days. But many people actually saw her. Some became alarmed and reported it to the police. Ma'am, was there a car parked up there? Hmmm. You mean you didn't see any vehicle stalled out there, anywhere along the bridgeway? Some yelled the apparition to tolltakers. *She was blond, right? At the top? Yeah, we'll take care of it.* Some just eased off the brake pedal, rubbed both eyes, continued home and began paying close attention to the news. *Three days. Nothing in the paper. Maybe they haven't found the body?*

And, as is the fate of most legends and ghosts, some made believe they saw her.

Watch out for the blond up on the bridge, the citizens band radios would crackle, *she's gonna get you.* What's she doin' up there? *Better not stop to find out.* Most regular "bridge-runners"—people who live in one county and work in the other—know about the blond if they've got a CB.

Over the years, she grew into a superstitious phantom, her existence based in the many suicides and other tragedies associated with the troubled bridge. An urban folktale, so to speak. The blond always appeared at night, often when the air was thick with wet fog. She always looked as if she had been atop the bridge for hours—her T-shirt clung tightly to her lithe body. And her hair was always wild and windblown.

Then came the black Friday in May when the Skyway's southbound span fell atop the empty freighter which struck it in a rainstorm. We can all imagine the horror of that morning: The headlights of vehicle after vehicle hurtling into crazy nothingness, the ship's pilot screaming "Mayday" into the radio, 35 bodies beaten bloody and drowned.

What about the blond? Was 7:34 a.m. a time she had chosen to appear on the bridge that day? Was her ghost given up with the others. Hardly. Such legends are embellished—not destroyed—by tragedy.

The blond atop the bridge is now a hitchhiker along its approach. I first found this out in an Italian restaurant in Rockledge, on this state's East Coast. The owner's wife told me a strange story about the Skyway blond. She swore, "The people who told me this are straight people. And they heard it from straight people.

"Otherwise I would never believe such a story."

I called the person who told her the story. Sounded like a very straight person. That person said it originated from a friend's friend. I called the friend's friend. Pretty straight. The friend's friend heard it from a friend's friend. And her name was Kathy Bridges!

I traced the story throughout Florida and Georgia, through at least 40 friends and friends of friends...all the way to St. Petersburg. To the source.

It was an elderly couple who live near Tyrone Mall. That's all they will permit me to say. They were hesitant to talk, worried about the embarrassment their story might bring. They would only talk with me over the phone, and only while their minister was present at their home, listening on an extension phone. I asked them to tell me what had happened.

"It was this summer. August," said the elderly woman. Her husband would not talk to me. "We were coming back from a dinner theater in Sarasota. It was about midnight."

It was drizzling very softly, the woman told me: "You know, the kind of rain that puts oil on the road. I was scared to death of going over that bridge. I was afraid we'd slide out of control."

Along the roadway, less than a mile before the span and half-a-span that rise above the ship's channel today, "there was a girl hitchhiking. She had a terrible look of fear on her face when we passed. I made my husband stop."

There was no car in sight. And the night was oddly quiet when they stopped the car. "She ran up and just got in the back seat without saying a word. We asked her where she was going."

"'I'm afraid of that bridge. I'm afraid to drive over it. I'm just going to the other side,'" were the hitchhiker's first words, according to the elderly woman. She described the hitchhiker as an unkempt blond, about 20-25 years old. "Her eyes were scary," said the woman, her voice trembling. "And her face was all scuffed up. I couldn't tell if it was dirt or bruises."

Because of the high seat-backs and headrests on the automobile, the woman says she could not look to the backseat very well. "We never did get a real good look at her before she..." Before she what?

"As we were driving up the bridge she started talking real fast, asking us about God and Jesus. She kept asking me if I loved Jesus. We didn't know what to say. She scared me. She asked if we were prepared to die."

The blond eventually grew quiet. "We just weren't talking with her about that subject. It all made me so nervous. Then as we were going down the other side, my husband said, 'Where's the girl?'"

The blond had disappeared. The elderly couple swerved in their car from lane to lane, trying to peer around the headrests. But she was gone. "When we finally got off the bridge part, my husband stopped the car. I thought, 'My God, she has to be down on the floorboards.' She was gone."

Disappeared. Just like she used to back when she hung out at the top of the bridge. And she left nothing in the car, not even a single windblown hair. The couple sped to the St. Petersburg tollbooth where they say they informed the night tolltaker of the incident. "You know what he told my husband? He said, 'Oh, you are the third or fourth car that's told me that one,'" says the woman.

"He thought we were joking. Or that we were nuts." Which is exactly what the tolltakers and policemen I talked to feel about the incident. "Whaddaya want me to do—say I believe in ghosts?" said tolltaker G.Y. Brown. "Personally, I don't think it happened. C'mon."

Did the blond hitchhiker really disappear from the St. Petersburg couple's car? Did she ever get in the car at all? What mysterious potion had permeated the senses of two "straight" persons and brought a vision to flesh and back to spirit in their presence? "These things are not always black and white. Nor what they seem," their minister told me. "These are not people who would make up a story. I believe them when they tell me they feel they saw this..."

Ghost? I offered. "Welllll," he struggled for words. "I wouldn't call it that. I don't know what you would call it. It certainly was real to them."

The blond on the Skyway bridge. Real or fantasy? If anyone sees her, tell her I said hello. I'd like to talk with her some time. Just to see if she's for real.

"The Blond on the Skyway Bridge" by Peter B, Gallagher originally appeared in *FLORIDIAN*, magazine of the *St. Petersburg Times*, St. Petersburg, Florida, January 18, 1981, pp. 6-7.

So You Don't Believe in Ghosts!

THE WIND IS HOWLING OUTSIDE and you're home alone. What was that sound in the kitchen? Better go out and see. No—it's dark out there. Better stay in here and turn the television up louder.

Nobody believes in ghosts any more. Nobody but me. And against my will I'm making a collection of Colorado ghost stories. Seems like anyone who has a haunt in his attic or basement or back yard wants to tell me about it. Why me? I don't want any more ghosts.

Colorado certainly has its share of bogies, spooks, haunts and specters. The Rio Grande Railroad is said to have owned a haunted locomotive. A dead Indian reportedly drops pebbles on you if you sit on Thunder Rock near Turkey Creek. There used to be a haunted silo, of all things, near Simla, Colorado.

Like the case reported in Folklore, No. F-10 (Superstitions; the Supernatural; Ghost Stories), prepared by the Colorado WPA Writers Program 1936-1942. It concerns a haunted mine, the Mamie R., on Raven Hill at Cripple Creek.

The Mamie R., the WPA researchers found, had a bad reputation in 1894. Three men had died there. A new cable had broken, and the falling bucket smashed a mucker "into an unrecognizable mass." Later a miner was killed in an unexplained blast.

Third, a man named Garson, who ran the mine boarding house, fell ill of mountain fever. He died nine days later. On Nov. 15, 1894, E.D. Blake was appointed boarding house boss in his place.

Thanksgiving night, Blake, Fatty Root, a foreman, and two other men were working. They were all on top.

Suddenly the signal bell rang three times, then one. This was the signal for "Man aboard, hoist away."

The hoist man started the bucket upward but before it reached the top of the workings the bell rang one time, indicating "Stop." Then it rang twice, the signal for "Lower away." Then came a bewildering mixture of signals.

Blake and Root hauled the bucket up, went down and went all through the workings. They saw no one. On their return to the top the engineer there said no one had come out, either.

A few nights later a miner was working at the 375-foot level. He came up to report that he believed a man had been killed in his drift.

He had, he said, placed a round of shots and someone had passed him, walking into the charges. He yelled "fire!" But the man had paid no attention.

As soon as the smoke cleared a party went down. They reported they saw a man with blood streaming from several gashes on his head. One of his arms was blown off and he carried it on the other shoulder, like a rifle.

They spoke and got no reply, so one of the party grabbed at the figure. His hand went through it. The shift boss poked a drill at the thing but it encountered nothing.

The specter went to the bucket and rode up. When the rescue party got their courage back they signaled for the bucket and went up themselves. The engineer denied that the bucket had ever been hauled up.

On Christmas Eve (and maybe after a little holiday cheer) Root, Blake, and two others again were on top, talking. The bell sounded.

"Who's down there?" Root asked.

"Not anybody!" the engineer said. But he started the hoist anyhow. The bucket reached the surface.

The WPA report quotes Blake:

"All three of us started back and the blood curdled in our veins...I hope to be spared ever seeing such a sight again.

"Garson got out of the bucket first, Garson, with his yellow, pinched face and staring eyes, just as he looked the night I saw him die of mountain fever.

"Then came the one-armed man, with the blood spattered over his features, and the shattered stump of an arm.

"Between them they lifted out the body of a poor fellow lashed to a plank and laid it on the platform.

"Then the one-armed man reached down in the bucket and brought out his arm. As he rose from the stooping posture he looked toward us, the most ghastly object I ever beheld, his face all cuts, his clothing torn to shreds.

"He laid the arm on top of the body that was lashed to the plank, and the two raised the whole horrible thing to their shoulders and walked out into the night.

"For a minute no one spoke, and then we all rushed to the door, and as true as I live, we saw the two dead men, ghosts or whatever they were, walk over the edge of the dump and disappear in the darkness."

The next day, Christmas Day, Fatty Root took the bucket dumper's place and was working away along toward midnight.

"They had just hoisted a dozen buckets of water and the 13th was coming to the top, when the winding spool slipped out of the frame and the cable came off in the coils.

"One of the loops caught Fatty around the neck, cutting his head off as clean as if it had been done with a knife.

"About a month later the mine closed down with the operating company losing much money."

There's a catch, of course. The State Bureau of Mines says it has no listing of a Mamie R. mine in the Cripple Creek district. However, the bureau records start with 1895, and this story is dated 1894. You draw your own conclusions. Me, I can just see that eerie trio disappearing over the edge of the mine dump.

"So You Don't Believe in Ghosts" by Bernard Kelly originally appeared in *The Denver Post*, October 28, 1962, pp. 12-13.

The Headless Frenchman

1614: ETIENNE BRULÉ CAME from France to North America with Samuel De Champlain about 1608 when he was 16 years old. He developed into a remarkable man with great stamina and fortitude. He has been called the "pioneer of the pioneers." He was a scout and interpreter for Champlain, was the first white man to see the Genesee River, and explored the full length of the Susquehanna River.

Brulé lived many years with the Indians. At one time he was captured by the fierce Iroquois, tied to a stake and a start was made in torturing him. They burned him with irons, pulled out his fingernails and started to pull his long beard out by the roots.

He called their attention to a Lamb of God medal he wore on a chain around his neck. He told them that if they did not treat him with kindness his God would punish them. At that moment there was a close bolt of lightning with a crash of thunder. The Indians decided his God spoke with authority. They released him and nursed him back to health. He continued to live with them for a time but finally wandered away to explore other areas and live with other tribes.

His end came while living with the Hurons, who never fully trusted him. After some dispute they killed him and ate him in a Frenchman stew.

There is a legend in the southern part of Potter County and in Clinton County that Brulé was there. H.M. Cranmer states it as a fact. Here is his story as it appeared in 1956 in the Keystone Folklore Quarterly.

"Of ghosts I have laid many, but some I failed to solve. Most famous ghost in the Kettle Creek area was the Headless Frenchman. He haunted the area at the head of Hammersley Fork valley in East Fork District, Potter County, at the Twin Sisters, named for two large white pine trees.

"Back in 1614-1618, when the Frenchman Brulé was trapped in Pennsylvania and could not return to Canada for four years, he and his men searched for a silver mine. The pit is still there as well as their smelter. The Indians killed one of his men and cut his head off. Ever after, the Indians claimed, he came back at midnight of the full moon in October of each year. In the old days no hunter would camp near the Twin Sisters.

"When lumbering was carried on there, several men at different times saw the Headless Frenchman. In 1948 I arranged for a party to go up and see the apparition. Over a hundred asked to go, but when the night came they suddenly remembered that they had not lost a Headless Frenchman whom they had to go 10 miles back into the woods to make a date with. So I went with a dozen schoolboys, taking along 20 pounds of weenies. An old gas well leaked enough to make a fire to roast the weenies. At 10 p.m. the ghost of the Headless Frenchman passed by!

"Being a natural gas country, there are so called 'breathing caves' in these mountains. On warm days air is drawn in, on cold nights forced outward. At times there is a small leakage of gas.

Being warmer than the air, it will not mix with the air until it cools. At a distance it looks like a ball of fire in the moonlight, but close up it shows your reflection like a fun mirror at a carnival; long legs, short body, and no head. A man walking down the railroad track and suddenly seeing a headless man walking beside him would start to run. Glancing over his shoulder to see how he was doing he would see the headless man running after him, then get out of the way rabbit and let a man run who is in a hurry!

"There I ruined a beautiful 300-year-old legend with my curiosity."

Did he? Does warm gas linger beneath cold air? Can a large

bubble of gas pursue a running man? Is Cranmer's explanation even more amazing than the apparition itself? What do you think?

Charlie Cross said he talked to some of the boys the next day after the trip. They told him they saw nothing unusual. If everyone spoke the truth it means Cranmer had psychic ability which the boys lacked. Not an unusual situation. There is evidence that he did have some psychic sight and hearing.

The Headless Frenchman remains an unexplained mystery. Some who saw the ghost said he carried his amputated head under one arm. Even today some Kettle Creek people are careful to stay away from the Twin Sisters after dark.

To confirm some of Cranmer's statements, Charlie Cross says that on the very narrow ridge between the Hammersley and Windfall Run, there is a stratum of some kind of ore about three feet thick. It is 30 to 40 feet below the surface and outcrops on the side hill at that level. On the hill top there is a shaft which is now about 12 feet deep and 20 feet in diameter. Pieces of the ore can be found around this pit.

Ira Weed told Charlie that when he was a boy, about 1880, he was there with Ferd Ely, a famous, old hunter and trapper. Ely said the shaft had always been there as far back as anyone could remember. When he first saw it, it was much deeper. There was a 40-foot tree in it with the limbs cut off about one foot from its bole. This was evidently used as a ladder.

In the Hammersley Valley, near the Twin Sisters, about one mile from the shaft, Charlie has seen a stone chimney where the ore was smelted. There was much slag there with considerable evidence that mining activity had continued for a long time. The stone chimney was destroyed by the C.C.C. boys for some of their construction work.

Charlie sent a sample of this ore to a chemist in Johnstown. He reported he found nothing important in it but lime.

Something very valuable indeed must have been found for men to work so hard for so long and carry the ore so far to their smelter.

Perhaps Cranmer was right. Perhaps Brulé and his men did find silver, but I doubt it. I have found no proof that he was ever in Potter or Clinton Counties but he was close at times. Perhaps it was a different group of Frenchmen. It is known that the French did pass through the Black Forest when they were struggling with the English for possession of a continent.

There are legends that the Indians found lead ore in several places in the Black Forest. Perhaps they dug the pit. But did they ever build a smelter with a stone chimney? Their usual method was to heat the ore on a large sandstone rock with channels cut to permit the molten lead to run away from the fire until it solidified. The evidence of that method can still be found on the ridge between Sartwell and Fishing Creeks.

Here we have a mystery, caused by time, which was no mystery at the time.

"The Headless Frenchman" by Robert R. Lyman, Sr. originally appeared in *Forbidden Land: Strange Events in the Black Forest*, Vol. I, The Potter Enterprise, Coudersport, Pennsylvania, 1971, pp. 8-10.

Haunted Places

Lake Pleasant's Haunted House

THERE WAS THE DREAM SOME day of large and comfortable houses, as the early settlers of Lake Pleasant struggled to tame the wilderness and hew their rough log cabins. Yet this, in the year 1815, was not to be. The most impossible thing they could have imagined was that a manor house would be placed among them in their young mountain town.

And then the impossible happened!

Philip Rhinelander, Jr., of the prominent and wealthy family of New York City merchants, owners of Township Nine, was twenty-seven years old when he came, with slaves and servants, to develop his family's holdings. The 300-acre estate he cleared and built overlooking picturesque little Elm Lake was elegant by any criterion. By the rough standards of the young mountain settlement of Lake Pleasant, it was magnificent.

A center hall with dark mahogany staircase ran the length of the mansion. Off the hallway were large rooms, two with huge fireplaces. In the kitchen was a vast elevated oven, constructed of clay bricks made on the premises across the water from the Elm Lake Place. Handmade nails, fashioned on the estate, were also used in the construction. Master bedrooms of significant dimension opened off the large center hall on the second floor.

The house was lavishly furnished with mahogany furniture and beautiful paintings. A melodeon and marble-top table long after remained in the ownership of Meade Sturges.

At the front of the house was a cut-stone terrace. A park stood at the side. Toward the lake, where the lawns sloped gently down, was a massive flower garden. Nearby were vast orchards where apples, plums and pears were grown, and a vineyard to furnish grapes to the family larder.

At the rear were the outhouses for the servants, with a private cemetery where they might bury their dead. Further back stood the stables and carriage houses. And there was a creamery, with wooden racks for holding milk containers, and barns for storing hay.

A pretty stream flowed down the hillside and through the well-kept grounds. Here it was said the servants performed their family washings.

Far down at the outlet of Lake Pleasant, near the present bridge on the main highway where the still waters cascade to become the roaring Sacandaga, Rhinelander built a grist and sawmill.

There were 100 acres of land in crops at Elm Lake. Cattle, horses and sheep were sent from New York to graze in the ample fields. And there were oxen and sleighs with wooden runners.

The mountains looked jealously down.

Philip Rhinelander, Jr., worked alike to develop his property and to help forward the affairs of the new community of which he was a part. If the public life of the landed proprietor was unquestioned, the fanciful legends that for years surrounded life on his Elm Lake estate now began to arise.

He had married Mary Colden Hoffman, daughter of the Hon. Josiah C. Hoffman and his wife, Mary Colden, described as a singularly beautiful girl. To them in 1815 was born Philip R. Rhinelander, who later lived in Vienna and died a bachelor there on August 12, 1839. A daughter, Mary Colden Rhinelander, was born while the family lived in the mountains, on April 7, 1818.

The conveniences and luxuries of the Elm Lake home were only the outward expression of the deep love that Philip Rhinelander, Jr., held for his young wife. But love was said to have been coupled with almost equally intense jealousy. People said the young Mrs. Rhinelander was kept virtually a prisoner in her lovely home.

From time to time, she would write letters to friends back home in New York City, it was said, giving them to her husband to mail. Once out of her sight, the letters were torn to bits. Lonely and heartsick, she found herself cut off from the outside world.

At times, she tried to get messages to people in other ways. Once, a lone pack peddler came to the door of the Rhinelander Mansion and talked to Mrs. Rhinelander, the stories relate. He was later found dead in a spring on the Elm Lake estate grounds.

Another story told of a washwoman, servant of the household, who was befriended by Mrs. Rhinelander. Later, she was found dead.

Rumors increased among the townspeople, most of whom had never stepped inside the awesome mansion at Elm Lake. Time and the retelling only served to embellish them further. If they were misconception, they were none-the-less intriguing. The mansion at Elm Lake was irrevocably enriched with a garment of apocryphal lore.

In the late summer of 1818, Mary Colden Rhinelander became ill. On September 7th, she died. Again rumors circulated among the townspeople that slow poisoning had been the cause.

Unwilling, perhaps, to be separated even in death from the wife he so dearly loved, Philip Rhinelander had a vault built near his mansion in which his wife's body was kept until spring, when it was taken to New York City for burial.

Philip Rhinelander remained on his estate until the summer of 1823. Then, shortly after being elected supervisor of the Town of Lake Pleasant for the second time, he was seized with paralysis and left for New York City, never to return. Seven years later, he was dead.

For about four years, the property was occupied by the Englishman, Thomas Wayne. Later, the house was kept partly boarded up and a caretaker was employed. Gradually, it became known that the house was haunted. Only the hard-headed believed otherwise. The evidence was too wide-spread and too strong.

Cows were still kept on the estate for some years and the caretaker caused haying to be done. At first, the men would remain overnight, sleeping in the lonely rooms of the deserted mansion, but the room formerly occupied by the deceased Mrs. Rhinelander soon became roundly shunned. In the inky stillness of the night, a woman could be seen coming toward the bed, with plainly audible grief-stricken sobs resounding. When the men reached out to touch her, the apparition was gone. On another occasion, when one of the local workmen slept in the same room, he was disturbed by the sound of rustling skirts, voices raised in animated conversation, and he could "hear her combing her hair."

Soon sleep in other rooms became equally disturbed. At midnight, a man could be heard mounting the staircase, the hard leather heels of his riding boots clicking sharply on each progressive stair. Sometimes, the ghost seemed to be turning handsprings. Or again, the very bed-clothes would be pulled from the would-be sleeper, and there were often the unearthly sounds of something being dragged downstairs.

Once, a ghostlike figure was both seen and heard making its way through the hallways and into the drawing room, where it seemed to disappear into the boarded fireplace. The men tore the boards from the fireplace but nothing was found. At another time, a pumpkin came hurtling down the long center hall, striking against the far wall.

After a time, Isaac Page was employed as caretaker of the estate. The day their son died, Mrs. Page went to their home, leaving one of her daughters behind to complete the chores. The young girl milked the cows, strained the milk, and put it in containers on the shelf. Suddenly, the candles used for lighting the room were tossed into the air by an invisible force. Armed with stove pokers, the girl and her father searched the house from top to bottom but found nothing at all.

In view of this strange occurrence, several women from the town agreed to stay with the Page girl the following night. It was a warm evening and the women walked outside in the park. Suddenly, there was a whirlwind in the leaves. Madly, it came swirling around the house and careened crazily off toward Mrs. Rhinelander's empty vault. One of the women fainted.

Even the men working in the fields were not spared. The

woman who used to wash her clothes in the stream could frequently be seen, it seemed, and it was said that she haunted the grounds of the estate. The farmers were always pleased to leave the place to its ghosts each night before dusk had fallen.

The Rhinelander family seldom if ever came near the place. Most of the furniture was eventually auctioned off to pay delinquent taxes. Some of it still remains in local homes.

One night, around the year 1874, the abandoned mansion, a mere memory of its former elegance, caught fire and burned to the ground. The sheds were left to decay. The International Paper Company now owns and lumbers the land.

The forests have long since reclaimed the grounds and the road to the site of the former Rhinelander estate is hazardous to motor travel. Surrounded by dense forest, the ruins of the once magnificent mansion exist close to the side of the unfrequented dirt road, difficult to find.

As for the ghosts? Perhaps even yet, on quiet, lonely nights when the soft pale moon is half-hidden at intervals by shapeless scurrying clouds, their restless, eerie forms return at midnight to haunt the impassive, secluded spot where once a lordly manor was their home.

"Lake Pleasant's Haunted House" by Ted Aber and Stella King originally appeared in *Tales From An Andirondack County,* North Country, Utica, New York, pp. 19-23.

A Ghost Guards the Treasure on Neahkahnie Mountain

ONE SUMMER AFTERNOON MANY years ago Indians near Neahkahnie Mountain were astonished to see two sailing ships approaching the coast. These were the first sailing ships ever seen along the Oregon coast and, to the Indians, they looked like "great birds" as they raced in full sail toward the shore. Suddenly, the ships drew close together, and, just beyond the breakers, they began to "thunder" and puffs of smoke issued from the gunports in their sides. After much noise and smoke, one of the ships began to list, and was slowly but surely drawn into the breakers and cast up on the beach near the foot of the mountain. The other sailed off over the horizon and was never seen again.

As the great ship lurched onto the sand, men tumbled over its sides and staggered ashore through the surf. All of the men were white, except one, who was much larger than the others—a giant, some say. He was black. To the Indians, who assumed until then that there was only one race, these men of different colors were a frightening sight, and they regarded them much as we might regard visitors from another planet.

At low tide the strangers straggled out to their ship and began to bring their belongings ashore. Among the items brought from the ship was a huge chest, so heavy and cumbersome that it took eight men to carry it. With great effort, they carried the chest a short way up the mountain, where they dug a deep hole. Carefully they lowered the chest into the hole. The black giant, whom the Indians believed was an evil demon, was told to step forward. When he did, he was struck down, and his body was thrown into the hole on top of the chest. The men then filled the hole with sand and returned to the beach.

The Indians, as usual in their initial dealings with white people, were friendly, generous, and peaceful. They welcomed the strangers to their village, offered food, and helped the men to obtain shelter for the coming winter. The white men, as usual in their dealings with people of another race, were quick to capitalize on the generosity of their hosts. They took food, land, and other belongings from the Indians and offered venereal disease, measles, and violence in return.

The sailors quarreled with each other and with the Indians. Eventually, an Indian was killed. The Indians retaliated, killing a white man. A balance, of sorts, was maintained in this way through two winters, but, during the third year, the tolerance of the Indians for their irascible visitors was finally exceeded.

When the sailors began, at will, to violate the Indian women, a council was held among the Clatsops, the Tillamooks, and the Nehalems. Before dawn one autumn morning, 1,500 warriors crept into the camp of the white men and set fire to their dwellings. As the sailors ran from the blazing camp, the Indians killed them all. The white men were buried in a huge mound near the place where the box and the black man were buried. It is said that after this massacre, the river ran red with blood for three days.

The Indians, because of their reverence for the dead, never disturbed the burial place of the sailors, and, because of their fear of reprisal as the white presence grew in Oregon, they refrained from talking about the massacre.

Because of their fear of the "black demon," they never dug up the huge chest that the sailors buried on their beach. To this day, no one is sure what was in the chest, but many believe that the ship was a Spanish pirate ship and that the chest contained a fortune in gold.

Considerable evidence supports the assumption of buried treasure near Neahkahnie. In addition to the Indian legend, there are records of Spanish ships, loaded with treasure gained in raids on South American cities, sailing northward from Peru, never to be heard of again. Mysterious markings carved into the rocks on Neahkahnie Mountain could hold the key to the location of the treasure. At Three Rocks Beach, in North Lincoln County, skeletons and remnants of an old sailing vessel were found. One of the skeletons belonged to a man, thought to be a Negro, nearly eight feet tall. Stone walls, masonry, and giant mounds of rock placed in the shape of an inverted "W" with a base nearly a mile long have been discovered by treasure hunters near Neahkahnie.

If the treasure is there, it has eluded an army of treasure hunters, most of whom came to Neahkahnie with a hunch, a shovel, and a wheelbarrow. A few have come with bulldozers and backhoes. Many have come with metal detectors. Five people, including Charles and Lynn Wood, a father and son who were killed when their 30-foot deep hole caved in on them in 1931, have been killed in the search for Neahkahnie's elusive treasure.

Some say that the treasure is there, but it will never be found. They believe that the ghosts of the black giant and his evil companions still guard the treasure of Neahkahnie and that they will keep the treasure hidden, forever.

"A Ghost Guards the Treasure on Neahkahnie Mountain" by Mike Helm originally appeared in *Oregon's Ghosts and Monsters*, Rainy Day Press, Eugene, Oregon, 1983, pp. 39-42.

Moosilauke's Ghost Story

THEY SAY THAT ONCE UPON A time the mysterious (and imaginary) Dr. Benton bought a house near the base of Mount Moosilauke and used the dogs and cats of his neighbors for research work in anatomy. However, his neighbors thought that with the help of the devil he was searching for the secret of the lost "Elixir of Youth," which he would discover by stealing babies and using their blood in his experiments.

One day, a local family's baby disappeared, so a mob stormed Dr. Benton's house. But finding no doctor and no baby, they burned down the house and went up Mount Moosilauke after him. They were driven back by a storm, but a few people swore they caught a glimpse of him silhouetted against the clouds, with his long cape flying in the wind and with one hand holding a cup which contained his Elixir of Youth, made from the blood of his baby victim.

Since then 'tis said he has often been heard and seen, for he cannot die because of having found the secret of youth.

Old Doc Benton was blamed for any misfortunes on the mountain, particularly for the mysterious burning of the Tip-Top House. Some folks say that it was probably hit by lightning, but how can they be sure it wasn't Old Doc Benton stirring up trouble? After all, the Tip-Top House had been anchored to the mountaintop with heavy iron rods and chains, which Old Doc now drags behind him, clanking back and forth across the mountaintop.

Storytelling

This tale, with variations and elaborations, was told to many generations of overnight visitors at the Tip-Top House and later at the Ravine Lodge preferably in front of a crackling fire on a dark, stormy night.

Zeke Moody says that at the Ravine Lodge, experienced storytellers used to station an accomplice outside in the hall with a small cannon loaded with ten-gauge shotgun shells, which he shot off in the middle of the story—probably at the time of the thunderstorm. Zeke's son Bobby even installed chains overhead, above the ceiling, attached to a cord by which they could be rattled on cue.

Jack Noon of the Ravine Lodge said that they are still telling the story to visitors on the mountain, including Dartmouth freshmen who are there as part of their orientation. The story is never told twice the same, but is generously elaborated as the occasion suggests.

Jack Noon's Version of the Story

Tom Benton was the son of two of the earliest settlers in the town of Benton. As he was growing up in the late 1700's, he impressed the teacher at the small school so much that a judge in Plymouth arranged to have Tom live with him, to read from his extensive library and to get ahead in his education. The judge was tremendously impressed with Tom's intellectual powers and tried to get him to follow law, but gave up on that after he saw that Tom's true interest was in medicine.

Doctors being scarce and badly needed in the North Country, the judge and other settlers from many of the towns through the Baker River Valley raised the money to send Tom to the finest medical school in the world, which at that time was the University of Heidelburg in Germany.

At Heidelburg, Tom had some difficulty at first in adjusting to the language, but after he had mastered it, he distinguished himself in his studies and rapidly rose to the top of his class.

One old teacher took a special interest in Tom and worked very closely with him during his stay in Germany. This teacher had been brilliant as a youth, and as a young man had enjoyed a fine reputation as a doctor. In his old age he had fallen into some disrepute among his colleagues because of his bizarre experiments, which, it was rumored, had to do with searching for the secret of eternal life.

The old teacher died suddenly, leaving Tom a small sum of money, a few clothes, and the contents of an old oaken trunk, which was filled with old books and papers having to do with the doctor's research. Tom scarcely looked at them while he was in Germany, but when he had completed his studies and returned to Benton to set up his practice he brought the trunk with him.

Tom enjoyed a few years of spectacular professional success, and had a variety of offers to set up practice in Portsmouth or Boston. But he remained in Benton, and patients from as far as 200 miles away came to see him, including some of the wealthiest and most influential people of the day.

Tom became engaged to be married, but when the girl jilted him he lost all interest in life and in his practice. He didn't seem to snap out of it even after several years, but rather became more withdrawn and let his practice fall off. He moved into a small shack on the outskirts of the community and became pretty much a hermit.

Strange Happenings

Some boys who set out one dark night to see if they could frighten him were frightened themselves when they peeked through his window. There they saw doctor Benton bent over tubes and vials, heating chemicals, and studying notes which were strewn all over the shack, but mostly near the large oaken trunk, which had its lid open. The boys were frightened by the wild look in the doctor's eyes and his long, stringy hair and filthy clothes.

Then one day an old milk cow died on a neighbor's farm. There was nothing unusual about the death except for a strange marking behind the cow's left ear—a large red swelling with a white scratch across it.

Later a pair of healthy draft horses were found dead in their stalls. They too had the red swelling with the white scratch behind their left ears.

A teamster returning to Benton with the corpse of a young man killed in a shipbuilding accident in Portsmouth stopped at a tavern in Warren at nightfall. While the teamster was inside drinking, the corpse was stolen from the coffin in the back of the wagon. A search of three days finally turned up the corpse in some bushes by a brook. There was a second corpse with it— that of a man no one had ever seen before in those parts. Each man had the peculiar marking behind his left ear.

Doc Benton disappeared about this time, although there were rumors that he was still in the area. Hunters said they caught occasional glimpses of him on Moosilauke. He had grown old and was wearing a black cape, and the cape and his white hair streamed out behind him as he ran.

Kidnapping

In the early 1800's a housewife in Benton was hanging up her laundry outside on a cold November day with snow beginning to fall. She heard her little girl scream, and watched in horror as a black-caped figure carried her off. Then the frantic mother roused her husband to give chase, while she ran to get the neighbors.

A large group of men on horseback and with guns followed the tracks in the snow. They soon caught up with the child's father, pulled him up onto one of the horses, and continued following the tracks of the black-cloaked man. They moved up towards Little Tunnel Ravine, where they had to abandon their horses. The tracks led up into the ravine, which is a dead end. The men were certain that there they would trap the kidnapper, whom many of them said was Tom Benton.

The tracks ended abruptly at the headwall. The men were confused, but suddenly a mocking laugh from high above made them look up. They saw Tom Benton at the top of the cliff. Slowly he raised the little girl high over his head and then threw her screaming down into the group of men below.

Superstitions

Many years passed after that, and Doc Benton existed only

in rumors as new generations came along. There were a number of superstitions connected with him, but no one saw him again.

Nevertheless, when Darius Swain and James Clement of Warren were building the Tip-Top House, they found it impossible to get the workmen to stay on top of the mountain at night. They simply refused, muttering something about Doc Benton. After the hotel was completed, there was a gala Fourth of July opening with many distinguished visitors. Swain and Clement thought they had their fortune made at the hotel, but as night drew near, all of the guests departed. There was still fear and superstition which kept them from staying the night. The stories of Doc Benton and the rumors that he was still living somewhere on the mountain were enough to drive everyone away.

Brave Men

Swain tried to remedy the situation. He went to Boston to hire a couple of tough men. He found two loggers who had just completed a river drive over on the Connecticut and who had traveled to Boston for some hell-raising and for a fling which would last as long as their money did. Their money had run out when Swain found them. He bought them some drinks, listened to them brag about how tough they were, then offered them money if they would agree to stay on top of Moosilauke for part of the coming winter. They jumped at the chance and said they would stay the whole winter if Swain would keep them supplied with whiskey, food, and plenty of firewood.

They had spent about a month on top of the mountain without incident when a tremendous mid-winter storm struck. For three days the winds raged. Then the winds abated and the snow stopped just as night was coming on. The moon peeked out from behind the clouds from time to time. Then the men discovered that they needed more supplies, and tried to raise Swain on the telegraph line they had rigged from the summit to Swain's farm. The line was dead.

The loggers cut cards to see who would go check the line. The loser bundled up and went out, with orders to the other man to come looking for him if he hadn't returned in twenty minutes. After half an hour, the other went in search of him, feeling his way down the path because his lantern had blown out. The moon came out at short intervals only to be blocked again by the clouds. The second man went a good distance before he tripped over something in the snow. It was his partner, unconscious. He hauled him back to the hotel, thinking he had been overcome by the cold, and laid him on his bed. He couldn't find a pulse, but he slapped and chafed the man, trying to bring him around. As he was slapping and rubbing, he chanced to brush aside the man's hair. To his horror he saw the red swelling and the white scratch behind the man's left ear. He ran screaming out into the snow.

Mr. Swain finally hired twenty men with guns to go to the summit together and spend the night. They drank whiskey and played cards all night. No one slept, but they proved they could stay overnight on top of the mountain.

Business in the hotel picked up and it became successful. There were a few strange rearrangements of rooms and furniture, but no bad incidents.

More Mysteries

The next Doc Benton incident came when Mr. Park from Dorchester had his gravity logging railroad on the mountain. A man named Tomaso, the brakeman on the railroad, was found dead after men down in East Warren came up to check to see why the train had arrived as a runaway without him. Tomaso was found a good distance from the tracks—farther than he could have been flung by the runaway train—and he had the red swelling with the white scratch behind his left ear. (Note: Mr. Park actually did have a gravity railroad on the mountain, and Mr. Tomaso actually was killed by jumping from a runaway car, as told in Book Three. The Warren vital statistics records don't mention the red swelling and white scratch—but who knows?)

One night the kitchen loft in the Ravine Camp collapsed unexpectedly with a tremendous crash. There was no accounting for how it had broken loose and fallen. Doc Benton, it was felt, must be to blame.

In the early 1970's a Dartmouth student was climbing alone

on the headwall of Jobildunk Ravine. He was found wandering in delirium through the Ravine by some concerned friends. He was in shock and had a fractured skull. His friends carried him to the Ravine Camp on a stretcher, and then took him to the hospital in Hanover, where he finally recovered. He never liked to talk about the incident, but it was rumored that he told one of his friends that as he was climbing up to a ledge, a hand had come out through an opening in the ledge and had pushed him. The doctors were concerned about a large red swelling behind his left ear, but according to the story there was no accompanying white scratch.

Doc Benton is still rumored to be around Moosilauke these days, though no one ever catches more than a fleeting glimpse of him.

''Moosilauke's Ghost Story'' by Katherine Blaisdell originally appeared in *Over the River and Through the Years: Book Five*, The Journal Opinion, Bradford, Vermont, 1983, pp. 176-181. Reprinted by permission of the author.

The Ghosts of the Opera House

MANY TALES OF THE SUPERNATURAL have their origins amid the rubble of lives cut short by untimely, unnatural or unexplained death. And, while many theories of existence on "the other side" discount these prerequisites, they continue to be part and parcel to a good number of "ghost stories."

This particular story begins with the most tragic and calamitous event in Berks County history. Let us set the stage with the account appearing in the Tuesday, January 14, 1908, issue of the Reading *Herald*.

> Death by fire in its most horrible form burst
> upon Boyertown last night. Over the Opera House,
> crowded with the flower of Boyertown's
> residents, swept a very hell of flame, gutting
> the building and carrying over 150 souls into
> eternity…it was too appalling for words. At
> one moment the happy, innocent folk sat
> watching the gay pageantry on stage before them…
> the next instant the hoarse cry of agony…
> and the futile endeavor to snatch one's self and
> one's dear ones from death in its most grisly,
> ghastly form.

And so, while reading like the introduction of a Gothic novel, the article simply attempted to put into words the stark reality of the Rhoads Opera House fire of 1908.

"Opera House" may have been somewhat of a grandiose

misnomer. The hall could comfortably accommodate about three hundred people, and was situated on the second floor of a building which housed the Farmers National Bank at ground level. In retrospect, it seems obvious that the room's size, location and ways of ingress and egress made it pitifully and eventually tragically, unsuited for auditorium use. There were fire escapes, but poorly marked and accessible only through windows. The width of the main doorway was only 46 1/2 inches, and the door opened inward at the base of a steep and narrow staircase. And still, the building's owner, a Doctor Rhoads, maintained that the building was fine for public use—even after 170 men, women, and children had suffocated, or had been trampled or incinerated at a Sunday School benefit play.

Response from the community was gratifying for the organizers of the show scheduled for that fateful Monday, January 13. Three hundred twenty tickets were sold for the semi-religious play, "The Scottish Reformation." Proceeds from the event would go to St. John's Lutheran Church of Boyertown. But those proceeds, as well as 170 human lives including the young daughter of the church's pastor, Rev. A.M. Weber, would go up in the smoke of tragedy that night.

Harriet Monroe was director of the play on that cold night, and the services of Henry Fisher were summoned to operate a stereopticon to achieve certain desired effects.

The gaiety of the evening was to be cut short ever so suddenly. So suddenly, in fact, that the exact cause of the fire is still a matter of debate. The sweep of the fire that night was so swift that no one knows for sure where the fire started. Some say the "magic lantern" of Mr. Fisher. Or a hydrogen tank explosion from a calcium light. Or coal oil footlights kicked over by a performer, igniting the curtain. Daniel Schlegel, a survivor, managed to escape through one of the ill-conceived fire escapes: "I saw exactly how the fire started. It did not start at the stage at all, but near the rear door.

"There was a noise like an explosion and every one ran for the door. When a large crowd was gathered at the door there was a second explosion and they were all enveloped in a large mass of flame.

"This caused a stampede, and it was not until then that the lights upset in the front of the building. All of the people then became excited as they saw fire on both sides of them. There was fire at both ends of the hall, but there was none in the center."

The Reading *Herald* said that after the Rhoads Opera House fire, "...all other tragedies in Berks County pale into insignificance."

Macabre descriptions of the tragedy colored the pages of newspapers across America. Tales of the "smells of roast flesh" and of the entire families lost in the blaze. The fire became somewhat of a "media event" in 1908 as major papers sent reporters to cover the holocaust and its resultant impact on this small Berks County town.

The fire claimed several notables: former Boyertown burgess Henry Binder, former Senator Dr. Frank Brunner, and Daniel Gable, a foreman at the Boyertown Burial Casket Company.

More than a score of bodies were never claimed, and many more were rendered unidentifiable by the intense blaze. In the cleanup process following the darkest night in the county's history, loose bones and body parts were collected and placed in a separate coffin which would join others in a common grave on the sloping hillside of Fairview Cemetery. Another morbid account confirms that the ashes of the building itself were buried, as they were thought to contain a good amount of human ashes.

As undertakers, nurses and police officers arrived from neighboring towns and cities, the borough was placed under martial law by Burgess Kohler. Police maintained tight security at the ruins overnight, fending off looters and ghoulish sightseers until the morning sun would bring light upon the grisly scene.

As the dawn broke, flags flew half-staff in the grief-stricken town. Aid came from a wide radius—money, clothing, medical—and the town wiped its eyes to start anew.

With more than 150 gravediggers standing by to bury the dead, the stories of the event began to take shape. Fact and rumor, suspicion and superstition all played roles in the ensuing, seemingly neverending unraveling of the details of the tragedy.

While not an integral part of our "ghost story," these details merit repeating. There were the entrepreneurs who quickly jumped on the scene. Artist K.B. Kostenbader published 11 x 14 glossy photo-art "souvenirs" of the tragedy. The United Traction Company of Reading was chastised for allegedly overcharging a bereaved relative for transport of his dead family members from Boyertown on the daily trolley run.

Rumors circulated that the blaze was a stunt to cover up a robbery of the bank office below the Opera House. This was quelled quickly. A Coroner's Jury suggested to the District Attorney that the show's director, Mrs. Monroe; the stereopticon operator, Mr. Fisher; and deputy safety director, Harry McBechtel, should each be charged with criminal negligence for being, in the jury's words, "inexperienced, incompetent and lax."

In a classic case of "closing the barn door after the horse has escaped," the Boyertown fire helped re-shape fire and safety authorities' thinking of fire exits, escapes and appurtenant regulations.

But let us turn our attention from the actual event to the bizarre stories which follow. Or, more properly, with one story which preceded the tragedy of January 13.

Wallace and Paul Gottschall were two young boys who managed to escape from the Opera House inferno that night. But, if their mother had allowed her intuition to govern her actions, they may never have gone to the show: "I was worried all evening and I was sorry that I had allowed my boys to go to the play. I knew something was going to happen. I could feel it in my bones.

"I heard the alarm of fire, and rushed to the front door. There I saw what I had expected. The Opera House was in flames. My two boys were in the building!"

Mrs. Gottschall's quotes in the next day's *Herald* are thought provoking, indeed. But the accounts to follow add even more kindling to the fires of the imagination.

The aura of tragedy in Boyertown that night conjured up many tales of ghostly occurrences, some of which were reported to the following day's papers.

State and local police called in to guard the borough while under martial law reported numerous unnatural experiences. One young woman pleaded for police help, saying she was haunted by the spirits of the Opera House dead crying out to her for help. The state troopers offered to watch her home throughout the night of the 13th, but still the woman would open a window every hour to keep a vigil for any ghosts who may appear.

An even more grotesque, yet strangely touching story came, too, from one of the state policemen detailed to guard the ruins of the Opera House, that cold, dark night. Once again, we shall let the Reading *Herald* tell the story:

> A man in his night shirt was found at 12:30 trying to enter the ruins. He said he was at home sleeping and that his dead wife came to see him. She told him to go to a certain place in the ruins, right where she sat, and that there it would be possible for her to talk to him.
>
> The man, who is an elderly one, has been worrying considerably because he could not identify the body of his helpmate. He said he is a great believer in ghosts.
>
> It took the combined strength of three state policemen to work him away from the ruins and take him to his home some distance away. He was barefooted on his midnight march and was very cold. A state policeman was detailed to stay with him all night.

What led the mystery man on his "midnight march?" Was it a fanatical love shattered by the sudden disaster? Or was the spirit of his "helpmate" indeed returning to beckon him for a final, melancholy meeting? And would it truly be a "final" meeting?

The building was rebuilt, reinforced, and reinhabited, and today stands in mid-town Boyertown as a reminder of this tragedy, a monument to those who died there, and, perhaps, a rendezvous spot for the spirits which rose from the ashes.

"The Ghosts of the Opera House" by Charles J. Adams III originally appeared in *Ghost Stories of Berks County, Pa.*, Mifflin Publications, Inc., Shillington, Pa., 1982, pp. 34-37. Reprinted by permission of the author; © 1982 by Charles J. Adams III.

The Dead Have Risen

The Ghost of Big Liz

IN THE MURKY LOWLANDS OF the Greenbriar Swamp in southern Dorchester county, as the legend goes, there is a chance of gold awaiting whoever has the nerve to meet and follow the headless ghost of an old black slave named Big Liz.

This tale has its beginning during the early days of the Civil War. A time when tensions and tempers ran high because of the divided sympathies of Marylanders.

Because many of the landed gentry on the Eastern Shore were helping the South run supplies past the Union blockade, plantation slaves were used by Northern forces to spy upon their masters.

Big Liz was a spy, and, so the story goes, a good one. Accordingly many cargoes of contraband shipped by her master were captured.

But her master found her out and determined to do away with her.

By telling Big Liz that he needed her great size and strength to help him bury his gold, the master lured her into the desolate Greenbriar Swamp.

After the gold was buried and Big Liz was smoothing over the earth, the evil master crept up behind her and crashed his sword upon her neck, cutting off her head.

Because he was afraid to return, the plantation owner never recovered his buried gold. After President Lincoln freed the slaves, the master died an embittered and anguished old man.

But since then, many people say, the ghost of Big Liz has wandered through the marshes among the tall grass, waiting to give away the gold.

What you should do, as the tale is told, is stop your car near a little white bridge over the Transquaking River and honk your horn three times. Your car will no longer start, and Big Liz will appear, holding her head in her hands.

If you follow, she will lead you through the trees and mud to where the wealth is hidden.

"But you will not have the nerve," the legend concludes.

The Phantom of O'Donnell Heights

IT WAS A BLACK-ROBED SPECTRE who crawled from among the tombstones of an East Baltimore graveyard to terrorize an entire neighborhood during the hot summer of 1951.

They called him "The Phantom of O'Donnell Heights," and his nocturnal wanderings over the rooftops of the blue-collar section sent teams of vigilantes into the streets, armed with sticks, shotguns and butcher knives.

He was reported hiding under automobiles enticing little girls to "come closer my dear." He was seen jumping from 20-foot high walls, but left no imprints on the ground. This galloping ghost vaulted over 6-foot graveyard fences, trimmed with barbed wire, and vanished among the tombstones.

During his two week romp, eerie, haunting music was heard coming from the graveyard chapel at 1 A.M.

Whatever he was, the phantom did not fear the armed mobs that set out to catch him, but openly defied them. He would come within view, and, like a wily fox, lead them on a chase.

One night the chase ended amid the moonlit graves. Several of the pursuers swore they saw the phantom jump into a sarcophagus. "He's returned to the grave," one said.

And as the August moon cast a pale glow on the tilting tombstones and the small crowded streets of O'Donnell Heights, the community began sleeping again in their second floor bedrooms.

Shells were ejected from shotguns, the butcher knives put back in the kitchen drawer, and the lookout posts went unmanned.

Somewhere a dog barked and knocked over a garbage can, but nobody started screaming. A baby cried for its 1 A.M. bottle, but then the lights were turned out again.

And nothing more was ever heard of the terrible Phantom of O'Donnell Heights.

The Drawbridge Ghost

THIS GHOSTLY SPIRIT WAS a free-born man of the traveling people, a Gypsy prince who lost his heart to an Eastern Shore beauty and was killed because of it.

Throughout the latter part of the Nineteenth Century and into the Twentieth, bands of Gypsies roved up and down the Atlantic coast, following the wind.

No wind was more elusive than the heart of this Eastern Shore maid, the daughter of an old and respected family in Drawbridge, a town in lower Dorchester county on the edge of the great Greenbriar Swamp. But the handsome Gypsy prince wooed and won her.

The girl's family opposed her. They could not believe this marriage could bring happiness, especially since there were so many young aristocrats beating a path to the young lady's door.

She, however, was adamant. Without telling her parents, the young girl went to the Gypsy camp and begged the prince's mother for help.

The old woman, reputed to be a witch, knew well the forbidden arts. She read the tea leaves of the loving couple, and saw death.

But she knew she could not change fate; death, if it really was there, would not be stopped. So the mother gave the maiden a wedding dress and a ruby headband that glowed like coals from dying embers.

Wedding days should be occasions of great happiness. But at the very moment the anxious bride awaited her lover his lifeless body was found in the swamp. Apparently he had been murdered, but no one knew how.

The girl returned to her family. She had lost her voice, and now lived the life of a recluse.

But exactly one year after the death of the Gypsy prince, the girl's eldest brother died mysteriously, and in his ear was found a Gypsy earring.

And every year for seven years thereafter, another brother died, inexplicably, sometimes even with policeman looking on. And on an ear of each dead brother was found a Gypsy earring.

By the eighth year, the girl still had not spoken. On the anniversary of all the deaths, a great darkness fell over her large plantation home, and for no apparent reason people were drawn to the house.

Many friends gathered, but said nothing. They just sat, as if in a trance and stared at each other.

Suddenly, as darkness fell, the tinkle of Gypsy bells was heard. And the music of a wedding march came from the woodwork. The girl appeared in her original wedding dress, with ruby headband shining brightly.

Slowly she walked down the great spiral staircase. Her father rose as if in a dream and took her arm. Together they walked to the door.

The girl fell dead. But a sweet smile of repose and happiness was upon her face. And on her finger, they found a Gypsy earring twisted into a wedding band.

And now, as many people say, every year on that August night to celebrate their wedding anniversary, the Gypsy and his princess gallop up to Drawbridge on a large white horse.

The neighing of the horse rustles the leaves and churchbells sound out the joy of lovers reunited in death.

(The next two stories are true, well-substantiated occurrences—and who is to scoff at any of the legends when such as these actually happened.)

White Marsh Church

THE CRUMBLING RUINS OF OLD White Marsh Church stand on a knoll only yards off U.S. 50 near Easton, passed unnoticed by thousands of hurrying motorists each day.

By night the ravaged walls and the ancient tombstones that surround them are more properly reminiscent of the strange and weird event that happened there more than 260 years ago.

It was in 1711 that the wife of Reverend Maynadier, the Huguenot rector of White Marsh parish, died. In accordance with her last wish, she was buried with a valuable ring, a family heirloom, on her finger.

Late that same night, two strangers who had attended the funeral returned to the gloomy burial ground of the church, intending to open the coffin and steal Mrs. Maynadier's ring.

The body was disinterred easily enough, but the pair of grave robbers were unable to remove the ring. A knife was used to sever the woman's finger. The pain, and possibly the cool, fresh night air combined to rouse the rector's wife, who apparently had been in a deep coma. She abruptly sat up, uttering a low, hoarse cry.

What effect this had upon the would-be ghouls is not recorded, but it can easily be imagined that they are still running.

They were never heard of again.

Fully revived, the stalwart Mrs. Maynadier wrapped her white shroud around herself and headed for home. One can only speculate and wonder what were her feelings as she trudged the dark road back to the rectory.

The Rev. Mr. Maynadier, seated before a fire at his home, was disturbed by a thud and a low moan as his risen wife fell against the front door. Overcoming his own panic at seeing the shrouded apparition, he caught his swooning wife and put her to bed where she soon regained her health.

Both the Maynadiers lived for many more years. They are buried side by side in the old church yard by the side of the modern dual highway.

The Floating Coffin

HOOPER ISLAND, A LONG NARROW spit of marsh and scrub pine, juts into the Bay from the Dorchester county mainland. The face of the island and the character of its inhabitants, descended from the early English settlers of the 1600's, have changed but little.

The area abounds in tall tales and legends, flavored and seasoned in the telling for over 300 winters around the coal stoves of general stores and hunting clubs.

Few of them, however, can surpass a tale of miraculous aid from the grave which actually occurred early in this century. It happened during the great storm of 1933, a fierce nor'easter that piled tide upon tide, flooding most of the low lying island.

One old waterman, finding himself trapped by the rising waters in his isolated cabin, had retreated in despair to the second floor of his nearly submerged dwelling to await the inevitable.

There came a gentle, but insistent tapping against the second story window. Again and again he heard it, strangely audible amid the howling storm. Finally he opened the window at whose base the waters already lapped.

The wooden coffin of his wife, recently buried, came floating into the room. The corpse, stiffened by rigor mortis, sat half upright.

Without hesitation, the old Islander hopped into the sturdy wooden box with his dead mate and set himself adrift. By morning, he had floated safely ashore on a neighboring island, his able, if makeshift, craft weathering the storm for several hours.

Part of the mystery was easily explainable, if bizarre. On the low-lying island, due to the constant water pressure only inches beneath the land's surface, the dead are buried on top of the ground. The storm waters had washed the coffin from its resting place.

But how it then floated, amid the dark and the wind, to the home of the waterman was perhaps explained best by the words of the taciturn old man as he stepped to dry land and safety:

"Thanks, old woman," he said. "You always did look after me."

A Ghostly Trio

IF, DURING THE STORMS OF LATE winter, you pass an old man in a one-horse buggy traveling through snowdrifts on unpaved Eastern Shore roads, you have met a doctor rushing to aid a patient who died 200 years ago.

The Talbot county doctor was an old man who liked his toddy and was wont at times to overuse it. But he always claimed he was a better practitioner when he was in his cups.

One night the doctor received an emergency call to care for a friend who had accidentally shot himself. The doctor had been drinking heavily to ward off the cold and wind of a heavy snowstorm.

It was a long drive. There were no roads. And the doctor, half-drunk, fell asleep.

The next day, he was found by a wanderer vainly trying to find himself and the home of his wounded friend.

"Oh, show me the way," he pleaded.

"Too late," the wanderer answered.

"Too late? Too late?"

"Yes doctor," came the sorrowful reply. "I just came from there and he died two hours ago, bled to death. You could have saved him had you arrived last night."

"Show me the way."

"It is too late."

The doctor promptly turned his buggy and rushed off through the woods. He was never seen alive again.

Later, his buggy and his body were found. A bridge had collapsed under him, and he was killed in the accident.

The people who lived near Easton buried the doctor in the Old Whitemarsh Cemetery, adding the inscription: "Rest His Soul."

The inscription's message apparently was not heeded:

Tradition has it that belated people who travel the highway where he met his death, on each anniversary of the December night on which he was killed, hear the hoofs of the old horse coming rapidly up behind them, hear the rattle of the old buggy and can see the misty outline as the spirits come close.

And through the snow and cold will come a helpless voice: "Show me the way."

The Ghost(s) of the Constellation

SITTING PROUDLY AT REST in Baltimore Harbor, the USS Constellation emits an aura of peace of security. Where once men died under the hail of grapeshot, children now walk.

During her 175-year history, much blood has flowed over her wooden beams. So what or who, among the countless who have met death on her deck, was the ghostly apparition that was photographed in the forecastle in 1955?

Lt. Cmdr. Allen Ross Brougham, USN, the man who snapped the photo, believes it is a captain returning to inspect his ship.

Hans Holzer, a professional ghost hunter and author, says it could be any one of three spirits "haunting the old ship."

To a Catholic priest who came face to face with the ghost, it is an old salt, unwilling to leave the beloved sea.

Legends of ghosts and other strange occurrences have long been told about the United States Navy's first ship. But the first indication that they were more than the reminiscences of old sea dogs came at 8 bells on a cold December night in 1955.

Commander Brougham had his camera set. Waiting patiently, he allegedly caught the ghost forever on film.

At 11:59:47 P.M., to be exact, the Navy officer "detected a faint scent in the air—a certain something not unlike gunpowder."

Then before him, he said, appeared a "phosphorescently glowing, translucent ectoplasmic manifestation of a late Eighteenth Century or early Nineteenth Century sailor, complete with gold stripe trouser, cocked hat and sword." He barely had time to snap the shutter before the eerie figure vanished, he said.

A few years later, repairmen heard strange moans and cries coming from below the decks, but every time they went to investigate they found nothing.

In Hans Holzer's book, "Portal to the Past," reference is made to the experience of a Catholic priest who visited the Constellation in 1964.

When the priest arrived, there was no member of the Maryland Naval Militia to take him aboard for a tour. So he went below by himself.

While wandering beneath the deck, he said, he was startled by an old sailor who volunteered much information about history of the ship and the proper names for the equipment.

After thanking his guide, the priest went above deck where he met several of the regular tour guides. He congratulated them for having such a knowledgeable man as the one who led him around.

The real guides were horrified. "We have no one below," they protested.

In haste, the guides and the priest rushed down the narrow stairway, but the old guide had vanished into the air.

Sybil Leek, the famous English witch, once paid a visit to the stately ship. She claimed she picked up vibrations from three spirits; a captain, a sailor and an apprentice seaman, who had all died violently.

Which one of these denizens of the spirit world was the one photographed, if any, is unknown.

Stories in the section "The Dead Have Risen," all by Joseph J. Challmes and Tom Horton, originally appeared in *The Baltimore Sun*, Baltimore, Maryland, October 31, 1972. © 1972 by The Baltimore Sun Company.

Ghosts, Coast To Coast

Spooks à la Maryland

IF YOU LIKE GHOST STORIES, the one about Stanford Hall is as creepy as any of the Maryland collection. It is taken lightly by the family who lives there now, and has never been written up, so far as I know.

Stanford Hall is a thirty-six room brick and stone house built by the well-known Mason family in 1734. It is grandly located on a hilltop overlooking Clear Spring about ten miles above Hagerstown.

The late Gov. William T. Hamilton owned it for forty-nine years, and it was purchased in 1920 from the Hamilton estate by its present owner Leo A. Cohill.

Natives of the countryside for generations have believed there is a secret room in the place and that disaster, probably death, will overtake anyone who finds it. There are several other spooky yarns about the hall and for that reason no native servant can be prevailed upon to spend a night under its roof.

There is a lady in silk, for instance, who they say appears sometimes in one of the first-floor rooms enveloped in a mist. The country folk whisper that they have heard the rustle of her silks as she made her accustomed visitations, walking serenely down the three steps which lead out from a rear door, circling the terrace and then returning and disappearing in the room.

There is another one, apparently about some ghostly moon-shiner, who, when all souls in the hall are in their beds at night, rolls a barrel slowly down the front steps.

But the really gruesome episodes concern the secret room. In 1924 the late Magistrate J. Scott Bower, of Hagerstown, an old friend of the Cohill family and a long-time resident of the neighborhood, told Mrs. Cohill the fable of this hidden chamber. He advised her to make no effort to find it, but he said he would come to the hall some day and take a look for it. Maybe he could settle the rumors once and for all.

Magistrate Bower did return a short while later. It happened that all members of the Cohill family were out at the time, so he went in and made himself at home, as he was accustomed to doing. He walked all over the house, the servants told Mrs. Cohill, and he seemed to be looking for something.

When Mrs. Cohill saw him later he refused to speak of what he had done that day. But this time he solemnly advised her never to seek the mysterious room.

Magistrate Bower died within the year.

In 1926 Mrs. Cohill's 9-year-old daughter, Margaret, who had long been curious about the room and was known to have spent many an afternoon hunting it, was taken critically ill. She died of heart trouble, and in her last hours she repeatedly begged Mrs. Cohill, "Mother, please don't ever, ever try to find that room."

"Spooks à la Maryland" originally appeared in *The Baltimore Sun*, Baltimore, Maryland, January 26, 1937. © 1937, *The Baltimore Sun Company*.

Horrors That Haunt the Northwest

ONE DAY IN THE FALL OF 1974, a prominent Seattle art dealer moved into a turn-of-the century mansion in an old section of Georgetown, almost in the shadow of Boeing Field. The big old rundown house had been vacant for more than a decade and he planned to restore and turn it into an art gallery.

During his first night in the house, however, he was awakened by a series of strange sounds coming from a second-floor corner bedroom, and the unmistakable cry of a woman's voice. The next night, at exactly 12:30, he heard the sounds again, this time even louder and more pitiful. The third night he asked some friends over and, at exactly 12:30, they too heard the eerie weeping sounds and the plaintive woman's voice which seemed to be crying the name "Manny."

He did some checking at the real estate office, and discovered that successive owners going back to 1910 had also heard the mysterious noises and the woman's voice crying "Manny" and had eventually fled the house because of them. He was so intrigued that he set out to research the history of the house to find some clue to the mystery.

One day, he found something in an old P-I (*Seattle Post-Intelligencer*) that made his blood run cold. It was an item about a murder that had taken place in 1899. It seems that in Gold Rush days the house had been a brothel and on one particular evening a young Indian prostitute had been brutally stabbed to death and horribly mutilated there by a young man who had been her lover. The murder had occurred at exactly 12:30 a.m. in the second floor corner bedroom. The young murderer's name was "Manny."

This story—which has all the elements of a classic ghost story and has been reasonably verified—is just one of thousands of cases of unexplained ghostly phenomena that have been reported in the Northwest over the last 100 years or so. Though these encounters never have been given the attention they might receive in older and more established parts of the world, they form a distinct body of ghostly phenomena which spectrologists (or ghost hunters) are beginning to call "Northwest Gothic."

In recent years such august groups as the Parapsychology Foundation and the American Society for Psychic Research have been looking into some of our long suppressed psychic incidents and have come up with some fascinating and rather disturbing results. Whether you happen to believe in this sort of thing or not (and the number of people who do is astonishing), the evidence is there for the looking and its sufficiently chilling to give a reasonable person a moment or two of hesitation before starting out alone this Halloween evening.

Tales of ghostly visitations in the Northwest, in fact, go back to the very dawn of recorded history. More than any other American Indians, the tribes around Puget Sound seemed to give considerable attention to ghosts. This fact was observed by the very first white explorers—Captain William Clark himself noted the peculiar fascination with spirits by the Indians of the region. The shaman was always the most important figure in the tribe and he engaged in what was believed to be a continual dialogue with the dead (most pronounced, incidentally, during the early weeks of fall). Writing in the "American Anthropologist," William Duncan Strong argues that an enormous "ghost cult" thrived on the Columbia and eventually "spread out over the greater Northwest." He claims that the entire culture of Northwest Indians—their art, dance and oral literature—was structured around worshiping and paying homage to ghosts.

When the white man came for good, Indian culture changed drastically but their ghosts apparently lingered on to exact some measure of revenge. Pioneers in early Seattle reported numerous inexplicable occurrences, most of them in the fall around Halloween and most of them involving Indian spirits.

The story is still told of a stubborn New England settler named Joshua Winfield who cleared the land and built a cabin in what is now Seattle's Mt. Baker area in 1874. His plot happened to be on the site of an ancient Salish burial ground and he had been warned from the beginning that many weird things had been seen there in the dead of night. One night he began hearing strange sounds, his walls began rattling, cold gusts of wind blew furtively through the cabin. Winfield, who did not cross the great prairie to be run off his land by a mere ghost, stubbornly refused to move and endured the strange harassment for more than a month.

One night a passing neighbor heard a shrill scream come from the cabin. Rushing in, he found Winfield stone dead, untouched, but with a look of terror on his face. No one ever knew what he saw but it must have been something particularly horrible because he had apparently died of fright.

These strange incidents continued all through the later 19th and on into the 20th century. Early Northwest historians prided themselves on being a forward-looking and unsuperstitious bunch, however, and most of these incidents were either ignored or consciously suppressed.

Some, however, have survived in local legend: In the '20's a stange apparition around Green Lake was connected to several unexplained and unsolved disappearances: an eerie crying sound, not unlike that of a baby, was heard for years around Kinnear Park on the top of Queen Anne Hill; on a beach in West Seattle, the form of an old Indian man materialized and then vanished before several horrified swimmers one day in 1933.

Mostly, though, such occurrences went unrecorded. Seattle may be the only city of its size in the country which has no centralized folklore file in its public library system, and, for the most part, these important psychic events have been lost to us forever.

But after World War II, a growing number of reputable scientists came to the conclusion that the whole concept of ghosts was not nearly as farfetched as once had been believed.

Various forms of energy previously thought impossible—atomic energy, ESP—were shown to exist. Perhaps some energy form of personality that we don't know about does survive death, particularly after a violent or unjust death. People began to take spectrology a little more seriously and soon many of these encounters were being fully documented. Of the cases that have come down to us, most seem to fall into one of four distinct categories: the benevolent ghost, the poltergeist, the haunted house and the phantom apparition (which seems to be either searching for something or trying to give a warning).

Benevolent ghosts are, unfortunately, rather rare in the Northwest. The most famous one was written up in a nationally syndicated column (datelined Seattle) by Westbrook Pegler. He tells the story of how the noted Colorado journalist Rufus Porter was riding the rails between Spokane and Seattle in December 1960. While huddled in an open car traveling across the Cascades, the temperature suddenly dropped to below zero and Porter nearly froze to death. Seeing a work camp near Leavenworth, he jumped out to seek shelter. He saw a light in the watchman's cabin and crawled over and pounded on the door. A strange bearded man with soft eyes let him in. The man seemed to know that Porter was on his way to Seattle and everything else about him. He fed him and treated his frostbite and would only utter one sentence: "I am your brother." The next day, when Porter got to Leavenworth, he told his story and found that not only had the work camp been abandoned for years but the watchman he described was long dead. He returned to the camp and the very cabin where he had spent the night and found not a trace of life. Had he imagined it or had he been cared for by a benevolent ghost? Pegler couldn't say.

The poltergeist (German for "playful ghost") is a generally harmless spook who makes noises, causes psychokinetic disturbances and is usually more of a nuisance than a physical threat. Volumes have been written about this phenomenon but verifiable cases in the Northwest are extremely rare.

In 1949, the Duwamish Bend housing project was terrorized by a wailing sound that may or may not have been a poltergeist. This ghost, which the residents called "The Voice," would sing songs, usually recognizable songs like "Blue Moon," "Fools Rush In" and (so help me) "Ghost Riders in the Sky." One journalist described The Voice as "deep, rich, captivating…as sweet as the note of a bell on a frosty morning…" Its nightly serenades continued for years and no one ever could offer any other explanation.

In 1970, an even more intriguing poltergeist in West Seattle got a great deal of press attention. Over a period of seven years, in a small, middle-class home, dozens of people had witnessed cupboards opening and closing, lights turning on and off, books falling out of bookcases and other psychokinetic disturbances. A medium claimed that the spirit of an Indian girl and her mother whose ancestors were buried on the site were responsible for the harassment. It is still totally unexplained and presumably still going on.

The haunted-house category is even more rare in the Northwest. Some Eastern states put out thick guidebooks to their haunted houses, but Washington is too young for such an accounting and simply can't compete. Port Townsend, however, has its share of legendary ectoplasms roaming the halls of its old Victorian homes. There have been stories about the Ezra Meeker Mansion in Puyallup and the Wilcuma Lodge on Vancouver Island. There have also been fascinating stories about one whole floor of a men's dormitory at the University of Washington being haunted by the ghost of a student who committed suicide there in 1958.

Probably the best documented haunted house was the one that served as the studio for the sculptor Alonzo Victor Lewis on Eastlake North. A local television personality of the time was so fascinated by the Lewis ghost that he tried to photograph it amidst a lot of ballyhoo back in 1952. Unfortunately, like most haunted house investigations, it turned out to be mostly show business and nothing came of it.

By far the most common phenomenon in the Northwest is what ghost hunters call the phantom apparition. These ghosts seem to be involved in some great unknown search or to be forever doomed to haunt some particular spot, seemingly materializing and dematerializing at will. There have been literally thousands of them sighted over the years—perhaps more here than in any other part of the country—but none of them have been more fascinating or persistent than the celebrated ghost of Glenacres.

For a period of perhaps 20 years this mysterious manifestation caught Seattle's imagination and was seen by hundreds of people, including a sizable number of police and press, in the area around 10th South and South 110th St. The apparition was gaunt, naked and was usually seen doing a haunting, Indian-like dance on the trail to the Glenacres golf course. For 11 of those years, Seattle police tried to catch this phantom and each time he literally vanished without a trace just as they got to him. Who was he and what was he trying to tell us? There was never a satisfactory explanation, except for the fact that some people believe the Glenacres course was the site—once again—of an ancient Indian burial ground.

The Glenacres ghost and all the others like it would seem to indicate that there is indeed a unique kind of Northwest supernatural phenomena. It has mostly to do with Indian spirits and it seems to occur mostly in the fall around Halloween, the time early societies believed ghosts and spirits come out to harm mankind. More and more, in recent years, ghost hunters and other devotees of the occult have been latching onto this virtually unexplored territory. Even Hollywood has gotten in the act. And this could could be only the beginning. Many spectrologists are actually claiming that the Pacific Northwest is the most haunted part of the country—the Transylvania of the Western Hemisphere.

Just why we have been so blessed is arguable. Part of the reason, perhaps predictably, has to do with the weather. The British author, Charles Higham, who recently published a book on the spiritual adventures of Sir Arthur Conan Doyle, is one of the many experts who have remarked on the similarity of the Northwest climate to that of the ghost-ridden England.

The other part has something to do with the mystery and inaccessibility of the region and is considerably more intangible. The Northwest has always seemed the most remote corner of the United States. There has always been a certain supernatural ambience connected to the region, call it an affinity for the occult. The first flying saucer was sighted near Mt. Rainier in 1951. The legendary curse of the Hope Diamond was largely created in Seattle in 1917 when its former owner, the actress May Yohe, was found working as a scrubwoman on Third Avenue. And, more recently, the Northwest Sasquatch has given rise to what seems an entire industry.

Whether there is any truth to these things only the people who have experienced them will ever know. All we know is that a belief in the supernatural has been an integral part of all cultures and seems, in a curious way, to be necessary for mental survival. Ghosts have been an outlet for our most romantic impulses and a metaphor for all the things we cannot understand. They are the direct testimony that there is "something" out there. And it is as real as the hope that life transcends death, as dark as our dark and insurmountable fear of the unknown.

"Horrors That Haunt the Northwest" by William Arnold originally appeared in the *Seattle Post-Intelligencer*, Seattle, Washington, October 31, 1976. Reprinted with permission of the *Seattle Post-Intelligencer*.

Footsteps of Idaho Ghosts

IN THE GUISE OF THE BULGARIAN monk of Bayhorse, the white robes of the Russian John spook, or the shade of Manuel Sato in the Boise foothills, strange things have flitted across the Idaho scene. They could not be ghosts of course, because there are none. Belief in supernatural apparitions is contradicted by the scientific mind. Goblins dance at Hallowe'en. Bony sprites jump in the moonlight. Eerie noises shatter the stillness of midnight. Stairs creak where nobody treads and shutters bang where there is no wind or human hand. All are figments of imagination, designed for the young at their revels or cunningly contrived by practical jokers to torment the gullible.

And yet there are in the lore of Idaho instances that lack adequate explanation. There may be complete solutions, as indeed there are in certain of the ghost yarns, but for some of the others, the veil remains drawn.

Legends of the Bulgarian monk crop out from time to time. Substance of this career is vague, as is perfectly proper for such an ethereal character. The person or whatever it may have been, is said to have inhabited an area of Salmon River near Bayhorse. He was known in that mining camp and at Bonanza on Yankee Fork as a recluse who seldom mingled with fellow men. He got his name from his garments rather than any ecclesiastical activity. The Bulgarian monk wore burlap robes, tied at the waist with a rope and topped by a hood that enveloped his face.

By all fragmentary accounts he was an amiable citizen, courteous when spoken to, honest in his infrequent dealings, and hospitable to visitors who chanced to his humble cabin off

159

the beaten path. When he did come to town he was pointed out to youngsters as a bogeyman, a role he appeared to enjoy. Because he was willing to chase small fry and make growling noises at them as they fled he was the ideal foil for sport.

The monk displayed remarkable talent as a foot racer. Robust and apparently young, he outran practically everything in the district, failing only to catch certain of the kids he chose not to catch. He feigned stumblefoot as he reached them. They dashed on, screaming in delighted terror.

One of these episodes brought on the tragedy and ultimate mystery. While charging after a pack of boys, the Bulgarian monk tried a shortcut over a boulder, slipped, and fell in the river. His robe was found in an eddy. He was given up for drowned.

Two weeks later a visitor from Bonanza expressed amazement at the report of the monk's death. On the very day of the drowning, he said, the Bulgarian was in Bonanza, a good 25 miles away, going through the same antics with the children of Yankee Fork. Were there two of a kind?

The monk was not to be found at Bonanza, nor did he return to his cabin near Bayhorse. Riders jogging along the trail at Five Points reported seeing a figure pacing the shore with a lantern. The figure wore the garments of the monk. When approached, it vanished. The figure was also reported seen between Bonanza and the mouth of Yankee Fork.

Facts have not been established. In all probability the monk drowned. But if he drowned at Bayhorse how could he have been at Yankee Fork at the same time? And who was that hiking around in his clothes? It's something that gives rise to campfire conversation in the Sawtooths.

The ghost story of Russian John is geographically misplaced. The ghost walked on Baker Creek, several miles down Wood River from the camp long occupied by Russian John and the ranger station at the same place named in his memory. The incident took place about 40 years ago, making it only yesterday as history of the Sawtooths goes.

A camper pulled in for the night. He cooked his dinner and spread his blankets. Horses in the meadow disturbed his rest.

They champed and pawed and squished in the mud. The bell mare was a particular irritant. She couldn't make up her mind. She trotted from one side of the clearing to the other, banging her bell every step.

The sleepless camper finally thought of a scheme that would put an end to the racket. He dressed, took a sheet from his bed, and crept to a patch of willows near the line of march the old mare was regularly following. He crouched in the thicket and waited his chance. The horses stayed clear for a time. Then he saw three coming for the willows. At the appropriate moment when they were within a few feet he leaped up, waved the sheet and let out a yell that would shatter glass.

The diabolical display was answered by a human moan. The moan came from the falling body of a sheepherder. He slid from his horse in a lump, fainted dead away. When he came to, the horses were quite gone. The bell was no longer heard. The camper guessed they didn't stop running short of Ketchum. He ran a little himself in surprise at seeing the herder.

As the herder came out of his daze he asked, "Did you see it too?"

"See what?"

"The ghost in the bushes."

No, said the camper, he guessed he hadn't. But the horses must have.

"The place is haunted," said the sheepherder. "I'm through staying here."

And as far as the man who told the story knows, he never came back.

The haunt of Manuel Sato troubled the gulches north of Boise every now and then for years after the packer was murdered more than 90 years ago. His body was found, cruelly cut, by the fire where he was cooking breakfast. A saddlebag containing gold from Loon Creek was half buried near the fire, suggesting that the murderer may have fled in alarm before he could hide or get away with his plunder. Soldiers from Fort Boise, legend has it, used to hunt for the rest of Sato's treasure. They found nothing because their search was interrupted by the voice of a man directing a packstring. There was no packstring and no man. Only the wind.

The phantom horses of Owyhee County rank high on the roster of beneficial spooks. The story, sometimes credited to Indians and again to early ranchers, has it that a rider who had long been kind to the wild mustangs of the bruneau got lost in a blizzard. He wandered for several days and nearly perished from cold and starvation. A rift appeared in the clouds. Across the open patch of sky moved a bank of horses, led by a white stallion. The rancher went in the direction they had taken and presently came to a trail that led to shelter and survival. Had he seen a cloud formation that looked like horses? Perhaps. That is the explanation of logic. Horses do not fly any more than ghosts walk. Nevertheless, there is feeling of mystery about the incident that is not removed from wondering minds by processes of rational analysis. The phantom horses are creatures of fable according to the prosaic standards of most people. Fable or tall tale though they be, they trot a lovely path into the enchanting land of haunting speculation.

"Footsteps of Idaho Ghosts" by Dick d'Easum originally appeared in *The Idaho Statesman*, Boise, Idaho, November 3, 1963. Reprinted with permission of *The Idaho Statesman* and the author.

The Portrait of Theodosia Burr

ON DECEMBER 31, 1812, THE beautiful and vivacious Theodosia Burr, wife of wealthy Governor Joseph Alston of South Carolina, left her husband's plantation and sailed north on the *Patriot* to visit her beloved father, the famous Aaron Burr, in New York City. In early January the vessel was accosted off Cape Hatteras by ships of Great Britain, then at war with the United States, but was permitted to proceed on its journey. The *Patriot* was never seen again nor, with any certainty, was Theodosia.

An angry storm that very night swept the coast of North Carolina. Some say that during the gale pirates boarded the *Patriot*, removed all valuables, forced passengers and crew to walk the plank, then sank the ship. But legend persists that Theodosia survived, that she was cast ashore in a small boat onto the Outer Banks, bereft of all possessions except a portrait of herself, and that, with her sanity completely gone, she was thereafter cared for by a Banker fisherman and his wife.

The years went by. In 1869 the strange woman became ill, and a doctor from Elizabeth City was called in to attend her. He did what he could, but is was clear that she had not long to live. As he was leaving the sick room, the poor fisherman's wife told the doctor that, as she had no money, he would have to choose something from the house for his pay. When he replied that he would like to have the handsome portrait hanging on the wall, the afflicted old woman sprang from the bed. "It is mine! You shall not have it! I am on my way to visit my father in New York, and I am taking him this picture of his darling Theodosia!"

With that, she grabbed the canvas, rushed through the door, ran down to the surf, and walked into the ocean. The next day, the portrait washed up on the beach.

It is fact, not legend, that the doctor took the picture from Nags Head to his home in Elizabeth City, that a descendent sold it to an art dealer who in turn sold it to a member of the Burr family, and that it exists today.

"The Portrait of Theodosia Burr" by Richard Walser originally appeared in *North Carolina Legends*, published by the North Carolina Department of Cultural Resources, Division of Archives and History, 1980, pp. 34-35. Reprinted by permission of the publishers.

A Strange Tale

"I AM AN OLD MAN AND HAVE SEEN some strange sights in the course of a roving life in foreign lands as well as in this country, but none so strange as one found recorded in an old diary, kept by my Uncle William, that came into my possession a few years ago, at his decease.

"The events described took place in a mountain town some twenty miles from Montpelier, the capital of Vermont. I have been to the place on the mountain, and seen the old log house where the events I found recorded in the diary took place, and seen and talked with an old man who vouched for the truth of the story, and that his father was one of the parties operated on. The account runs in this wise:"

January 7: I went on the mountain today, and witnessed what to me was horrible sight. It seems that the dwellers there who are unable, either from age or other reasons, to contribute to the support of their families, are disposed of in the Winter months in a manner that will shock the one who reads this diary, unless that person lives in that vicinity. I will describe what I saw. Six persons, four men and two women, one of the men a cripple about thirty-six-years-old, the other five past the age of usefulness, lay on the earthy floor of the cabin drugged into insensibility, while members of their family were gathered about them in apparent indifference. In a short time the unconscious bodies were inspected by several old people, who said, "They are ready." They were then stripped of all their clothing, except a single garment. Then the bodies were carried outside, and laid on logs exposed to the bitter cold mountain air, the operation having been delayed several days for suitable weather.

It was night when the bodies were carried out, and the full moon, occasionally obscured by flying clouds, shone on their upturned ghastly faces, and a horrible fascination kept me by the bodies as long as I could endure the severe cold.

Soon the noses, ears and fingers began to turn white, then the limbs and face assumed a tallowy look. I could stand the cold no longer, and went inside, where I found the friends in cheerful conversation.

In about an hour I went out and looked at the bodies; they were fast freezing. Again I went inside, where the men were smoking their clay pipes, but silence had fallen on them; perhaps they were thinking of the time when their turn would come to be cared for in the same way. One by one they at last lay down on the floor and went to sleep. It seemed a horrible nightmare to me, and I could not think of sleep. I could not shut out the sight of those freezing bodies outside, neither could I bear to be in darkness, but I piled on the wood in the cavernous fireplace, and, seated on a shingle block, passed the dreary night, terror-stricken by the horrible sights I had witnessed.

January 8: Day came at length, but did not dissipate the terror that filled me. The frozen bodies became visible, white as the snow that lay in huge drifts about them. The women gathered about the fire and soon commenced preparing breakfast. The men awoke and, conversation again commencing, affairs assumed a more cheerful aspect. After breakfast the men lighted their pipes, and some of them took a yoke of oxen and went off toward the forest, while others proceeded to nail together boards, making a box about ten feet long and half as high and wide. When this was completed they placed about two feet of straw in the bottom; then they laid three of the frozen bodies on the straw. Then the faces and upper part of the bodies were covered with a cloth, then more straw was put in the box, and the other three bodies placed on top and covered the same as the first ones, with cloth and straw. Boards were then firmly nailed on the top, to protect the bodies from being injured by carnivorous animals that make their home on these mountains.

By this time the men who went off with the ox-team returned with a huge load of spruce and hemlock boughs, which they unloaded at the foot of a steep ledge; came to the house and loaded the box containing the bodies on the sled, and drew it to the foot of the ledge, near the load of boughs. These were soon piled on and around the box, and it was left to be covered with snow, which I was told would lie in drifts twenty feet deep over this rude tomb. "We shall want our men to plant our corn next spring," said a youngish-looking woman, the wife of one of the frozen men, "and if you want to see them resuscitated you come here about the 10th of next May."

With this agreement I left the mountaineers, living and frozen, to their fate, and returned to my home in Boston, where it was weeks before I was fairly myself, as my thoughts would return to that mountain with its awful sepulchre.

"Turning the leaves of the old diary to the date of May 10, the following entry was found:"

May 10: I arrived here at 10 a.m., after riding about four hours over muddy, unsettled roads. The weather is warm and pleasant, most of the snow is gone, except here and there drifts in the fence corners and hollows, but nature is not yet dressed in green. I found the same parties here that I left last January, ready to disinter the bodies of their friends. I had no expectations of finding any life there, but a feeling that I could not resist impelled me to come and see. We repaired at once to the well-remembered spot at the ledge. The snow had melted from the top of the brush, but still lay deep around the bottom of the pile. The men commenced work at once, some shoveling away the snow and others tearing away the brush. Soon the box was visible. The cover was taken off, the layers of straw removed, and the bodies, frozen and apparently lifeless, lifted out and laid on the snow. Large troughs made out of hemlock logs were placed nearby, filled with tepid water, into which the bodies were separately placed, with the head slightly raised. Boiling water was then poured into the trough from kettles hung on poles nearby, until the water in the trough was as hot as I could hold my hand in. Hemlock boughs had been put in the boiling water in such quantities that they had given the water the color of wine. After lying in this bath about an hour, color began to return to the bodies, when all hands began rubbing and chafing them. This continued about another hour, when a slight twitching of the muscles of the face and limbs, followed by audible gasps, showed that life was not quenched, and that vitality was returning. Spirits were then given in small quantities, and allowed to trickle down their throats. Soon they could swallow, and more was given them, when their eyes opened, and they began to talk, and finally sat up in their bathtubs. They were then taken out and assisted to the house, where after a heavy dinner they seemed as well as ever, and in nowise injured, but rather refreshed, by their long sleep of four months.

Truly, truth is stranger than fiction.

"A Strange Tale," told by an old man identified only as "A.M.," originally appeared on the front page of the December 21, 1887 issue of the Montpelier *Argus and Patriot*. A version of it was later published in *Mischief in the Mountains*, 1970, *Vermont Life Magazine*, Montpelier, Vermont, pp. 53-58. Reprinted with permission of *Vermont Life Magazine*.

The Jingling Hole

DURING THE WAR BETWEEN THE States, when the Potter-Stanfield feud was raging in the upper part of Johnson County, the Bloody Third rang with rifle shots from the skirmishes of the guns in battle, and the members of the victorious parties brought their prisoners across the hills. These victims were tortured, imprisoned or killed outright.

In the torturing process, the cave, called the Jingling Hole, played a most unique part. Since this cave has a straight descent of ninety feet, the victorious party—whether Potter or Stanfield—often placed an iron rod across the entrance. To this rod the culprit was forced to swing by his hands while his gloating captor tapped on his knuckles with the breech of his rifle, first on one hand and then on the other in rapid succession, causing an active display of gymnastics as the prisoner swung from hand to hand. Usually these victims were able to stand this torture and were released with bruised and blistered hands, to be preserved for future adventures; again, there was a casualty, as the victim rolled into the lake at the bottom of the cave.

The neighbors say that at night when they go 'possum hunting in the fall, they hear strange noises around the Jingling Hole. If they listen carefully they hear moans and groans, especially if the wind is blowing, and there is also the hollow sound of a gun breech cracking on knuckles, for the spirits of the Potters and Stanfields are not at rest but must still be torturing their victims.

This untitled story originally appeared in *Ghost Stories From the American South*, W.K. McNeil, August House, Inc., Little Rock, Arkansas, 1985, p. 57.

Heavy Collar and the Ghost Woman

THE BLOOD CAMP WAS ON OLD Man's River, where Fort McLeod now stands. A party of seven men started to war toward the Cypress Hills. Heavy Collar was the leader. They went around the Cypress Mountains, but found no enemies and started back toward their camp. On their homeward way, Heavy Collar used to take the lead.

He would go out far ahead on the high hills, and look over the country, acting as scout for the party. At length they came to the south branch of the Saskatchewan River, above Seven Persons' Creek. In those days there were many war parties about, and this party travelled concealed as much as possible in the coulees and low places.

As they were following up the river, they saw at a distance three old bulls lying down close to a cut bank. Heavy Collar left his party, and went out to kill one of these bulls, and when he had come close to them, he shot one and killed it right there.

He cut it up, and, as he was hungry, he went down into a ravine below him, to roast a piece of meat; for he had left his party a long way behind, and night was now coming on. As he was roasting the meat, he thought, for he was very tired, "It is a pity I did not bring one of my young men with me. He could go up on that hill and get some hair from that bull's head, and I could wipe out my gun." While he sat there thinking this, and talking to himself, a bunch of this hair came over to him through the air, and fell on the ground right in front of him. When this happened, it frightened him a little; for he thought that perhaps some of his enemies were close by, and had thrown the bunch of hair at him. After a little while, he took the hair, and cleaned his gun and loaded it, and then sat and watched for a time. He was uneasy, and at length decided that he would go on further up the river, to see what he could discover. He went on, up the stream, until he came to the mouth of the St. Mary's River. It was now very late in the night, and he was very tired, so he crept into a large bunch of rye-grass to hide and sleep for the night.

The summer before this, the Blackfeet (Sik-si-kau) had been camped on this bottom, and a woman had been killed in this same patch of rye-grass where Heavy Collar had lain down to rest. He did not know this, but still he seemed to be troubled that night.

He could not sleep. He could always hear something, but what it was he could not make out. He tried to go to sleep, but as soon as he dozed off he kept thinking he heard something in the distance. He spent the night there, and in the morning when it became light, there he saw right beside him the skeleton of the woman who had been killed the summer before.

That morning he went on, following up the stream to Belly River. All day long as he was travelling, he kept thinking about his having slept by this woman's bones. It troubled him. He could not forget it. At the same time he was very tired, because he had walked so far and had slept so little. As night came on, he crossed over to an island, and determined to camp for the night.

At the upper end of the island was a large tree that had drifted down and lodged, and in a fork of this tree he built his fire, and got in a crotch of one of the forks, and sat with his back to the fire, warming himself, but all the time he was thinking about the woman he had slept beside the night before. As he sat there, all at once he heard over beyond the tree, on the other side of the fire, a sound as if something was being dragged toward him along the ground. It sounded as if a piece of a lodge were being dragged over the grass. It came closer and closer.

Heavy Collar was scared. He was afraid to turn his head and look back to see what it was that was coming. He heard the noise come up to the tree in which his fire was built, and then it stopped, and all at once he heard someone whistling a tune. He turned around and looked toward the sound, and there, sitting on the other fork of the tree, right opposite to him, was the pile of bones by which he had slept, only now all together in the shape of a skeleton. This ghost had on it a lodge covering. The string, which is tied to the pole, was fastened about the ghost's neck; the wings of the lodge stood out on either side of its head, and behind it the lodge could be seen, stretched out and fading away into the darkness. The ghost sat on the old dead limb and whistled its tune, and as it whistled, it swung its legs in time to the tune.

When Heavy Collar saw this, his heart almost melted away. At length he mustered up courage, and said: "Oh ghost, go away, and do not trouble me. I am very tired; I want to rest." The ghost paid no attention to him, but kept on whistling, swinging its legs in time to the tune. Four times he prayed to her, saying: "Oh ghost, take pity on me! Go away and leave me alone. I am tired; I want to rest." The more he prayed, the more the ghost whistled and seemed pleased, swinging her legs, and turning her head from side to side, sometimes looking down at him, and sometimes up at the stars, and all the time whistling.

When he saw that she took no notice of what he said, Heavy Collar got angry at heart, and said, "Well, ghost, you do not listen to my prayers, and I shall have to shoot you to drive you away." With that he seized his gun, and throwing it to his shoulder, shot right at the ghost. When he shot at her, she fell over backward into the darkness, screaming out: "Oh Heavy Collar, you have shot me, you have killed me! You dog, Heavy Collar! There is no place on this earth where you can go that I will not find you; no place that you can hide that I will not come."

As she fell back and said this, Heavy Collar sprang to his feet, and ran away as fast as he could. She called after him: "I have been killed once, and now you are trying to kill me again. Oh Heavy Collar!" As he ran away, he could still hear her angry words following him, until at last they died away in the distance. He ran all night long, and whenever he stopped to breathe and listen, he seemed to hear in the distance the echoes of her voice.

All he could hear was, "Oh Heavy Collar!" and then he would rush away again. He ran until he was all tired out, and by this time it was daylight. He was now quite a long way below Fort McLeod. He was very sleepy, but dared not lie down, for he remembered that the ghost had said that she would follow him. He kept walking on for some time, and then sat down to rest, and at once fell asleep.

Before he had left his party, Heavy Collar had said to his young men: "Now remember, if any one of us should get separated from the party, let him always travel to the Belly River Buttes. There will be our meeting-place." When their leader did not return to them, the party started across the country and went toward the Belly River Buttes. Heavy Collar had followed the river up, and had gone a long distance out of his way; and when he awoke from his sleep, he too started straight for the Belly River Buttes, as he had said he would.

When his party reached the Buttes, one of them went up on top of the hill to watch. After a time, as he looked down the river, he saw two persons coming, and as they nearer, he saw that one of them was Heavy Collar, and by his side was a woman. The watcher called up the rest of the party, and said to them: "Here comes our chief. He has had luck. He is bringing a woman with him. If he brings her into camp, we will take her away from him." And they all laughed. They supposed that he had captured her. They went down to the camp, and sat about the fire, looking at the two people coming, and laughing among themselves at the idea of their chief bringing in a woman. When the two persons had come close, they could see that Heavy Collar was walking fast, and the woman would walk by his side a little way, trying to keep up, and then would fall behind, and then trot along to catch up to him again. Just before the pair reached camp there was a deep ravine that they had to cross. They went down into this side by side, and then Heavy Collar came up out of it alone, and came on into the camp.

When he got there, all the young men began to laugh at him and to call out, "Heavy Collar, where is your woman?" He looked at them for a moment, and then said: "Why, I have no woman. I do not understand what you are talking about." One of them said: "Oh, he has hidden her in that ravine. He was afraid to bring her into camp." Another said, "Where did you capture her, and what tribe does she belong to?" Heavy Collar looked from one to another, and said: "I think you are all crazy. I have taken no woman. What do you mean?" The young man said: "Why, that woman that you had with you just now; where did you get her, and where did you leave her? Is she down in the coulee? We all saw her, and it is no use to deny that she was with you. Come now, where is she?" When they said this, Heavy Collar's heart grew very heavy, for he knew that it must have been the ghost woman; and he told them the story. Some of the young men could not believe this, and they ran down to the ravine, where they had last seen the woman. There they saw in the soft dirt the tracks made by Heavy Collar, when he went down into the ravine, but there were no other tracks near his, where they had all seen the woman walking. When they found that it was a ghost that had come along with Heavy Collar, they resolved to go back to their main camp. The party had been out so long that their moccasins were all worn out, and some of them were footsore, so that they could not travel fast, but at last they came to the cut banks, and there found their camp—seven lodges.

That night, after they had reached camp, they were inviting each other to feasts. It was getting pretty late in the night, and the moon was shining brightly, when one of the Bloods called out for Heavy Collar to come and eat with him. Heavy Collar shouted, "Yes, I will be there pretty soon." He got up and went out of the lodge, and went a little way from it, and sat down. While he was sitting there, a big bear walked out of the brush close to him. Heavy Collar felt around him for a stone to throw at the bear, so as to scare it away, for he thought it had not seen him. As he was feeling about, his hand came upon a piece of bone, and he threw this over at the bear, and hit it. Then the bear spoke, and said: "Well, well, well, Heavy Collar; you have killed me once, and now here you are hitting me again. Where is there a place in this world where you can hide from me? I will find you, I don't care where you may go." When Heavy Collar heard this, he knew it was the ghost woman, and he jumped up and ran toward his lodge, calling out, "Run, run! A ghost bear is upon us!"

All the people in the camp ran to his lodge, so that it was crowded full of people. There was a big fire in the lodge, and the wind was blowing hard from the west. Men, women, and children were huddled together in the lodge, and were very much afraid of the ghost. They could hear her walking toward the lodge, grumbling, and saying: "I will kill all these dogs. Not one of them shall get away." The sounds kept coming closer and closer, until they were right at the lodge door. Then she said, "I will smoke you to death." And as she said this, she moved the poles, so that the wings of the lodge turned toward the west, and the wind could blow in freely through the smoke hole. All this time she was threatening terrible things against them. The lodge began to get full of smoke, and the children were crying, and all were in great distress—almost suffocating. So they said, "Let us lift one man up here inside, and let him try to fix the ears, so that the lodge will get clear of smoke." They raised a man up, and he was standing on the shoulders of the others, and, blinded and half strangled by smoke, was trying to turn the wings. While he was doing this, the ghost suddenly hit the lodge a blow, and said, "Un!" and this scared the people who were holding the man, and they jumped and let him go, and he fell down. Then the people were in despair, and said, "It is no use; she is resolved to smoke us to death." All the time the smoke was getting thicker in the lodge.

Heavy Collar said: "Is it possible that she can destroy us? Is there no one here who has some strong dream power that can overcome this ghost?"

His mother said: "I will try to do something. I am older than any of you, and I will see what I can do." So she got down her medicine bundle and painted herself, and got out a pipe and filled it and lighted it, and stuck the stem out through the lodge door, and sat there and began to pray to the ghost woman. She said: "Oh ghost, take pity on us, and go away. We have never wronged you, but you are troubling us and frightening our children. Accept what I offer you, and leave us alone."

A voice came from behind the lodge and said: "No, no, no;

you dogs, I will not listen to you. Every one of you must die."

The old woman repeated her prayer: "Ghost, take pity on us. Accept this smoke and go away."

Then the ghost said: "How can you expect me to smoke, when I am way back here? Bring that pipe out here. I have no long bill to reach around the lodge." So the old woman went out of the lodge door, and reached out the stem of the pipe as far as she could reach around toward the back of the lodge. The ghost said: "No, I do not wish to go around there to where you have that pipe. If you want me to smoke it, you must bring it here." The old woman went around the lodge toward her, and the ghost woman began to back away, and said, "No, I do not smoke that kind of a pipe." And when the ghost started away, the old woman followed her, and she could not help herself.

She called out, "Oh my children, the ghost is carrying me off!" Heavy Collar rushed out, and called to the others, "Come, and help me take my mother from the ghost." He grasped his mother about the waist and held her, and another man took him by the waist, and another him, until they were all strung out, one behind the other, and all following the old woman, who was following the ghost woman, who was walking away.

All at once the old woman let go of the pipe, and fell over dead. The ghost disappeared, and they were troubled no more by the ghost woman.

"Heavy Collar and the Ghost Woman" by George Bird Grinnell originally appeared in *Blackfoot Lodge Tales: The Story of a Prairie People*, University of Nebraska Press, Lincoln, Nebraska, 1962, pp. 70-77.

Fateful Vengeance

The Legend of Vivia

As Dawn First Broke On A bitter cold morning in January 1870, a guard patrolling the grounds surrounding Fort Gibson, Indian Territory, rushed to report to the commanding officer. He had found the frozen body of young Private Thomas lying across a grave in the cemetery near the fort.

The body was taken to the fort's infirmary. As it was being examined to determine the cause of death, a most unusual discovery was made. Private Thomas, who had enlisted only a few weeks earlier, was found during the examination to be a woman. As the commanding officer and his staff were reviewing these strange circumstances and wondering how Thomas had succeeded in passing herself off as a man, an old priest at the fort came forward with one of the most romantic and unusual stories in the annals of military history. Young Thomas had related her secret to the priest in confidence only a few days prior to her death. The priest's story was the beginning of the legend of Vivia that has been told ever since by families living in and around Fort Gibson in what is now eastern Oklahoma.

Vivia Thomas was the high-spirited daughter of a wealthy Boston family. She had been educated at the finest schools in the East and regularly attended Boston society's finest affairs. It was at one of the many Boston society balls that were held during the years following the Civil War that Vivia met and fell in love with a handsome young lieutenant.

After several months of courtship, their engagement and marriage plans were announced at a ball in their honor. Shortly before their wedding date, however, the lieutenant, who had been more intrigued by Vivia's wealth and place in society than by her beauty, suddenly disappeared. He left Vivia a note explaining that he was going west in search of adventure, which he preferred to marriage and the security of Boston society.

Brokenhearted and seeking revenge for the embarrassment caused her and her family, Vivia left home in search of the lover who had betrayed her. When she learned that the lieutenant had been stationed at Fort Gibson, Indian Territory, her long journey began. The trip was extremely difficult, especially for a Boston girl who had known only luxury during her pampered youth, but Vivia's vengeful heart pushed her onward.

During the months of her journey she cut her hair in a manly fashion and dressed in men's attire. At first her motive for disguising herself as a man was to provide the protection a male appearance offered as she traveled through the rugged frontier into Indian Territory. But her disguise had proven so successful that she decided to use it to get close to her faithless lover by enlisting in the Army at Fort Gibson. Her trick worked, and when she reached the fort she was enlisted in the U.S. Cavalry under an assumed first name.

During the months that followed, Vivia somehow avoided detection; her former lover never recognized her. She carefully observed him, all the while deciding how she would satisfy the burning hatred within her.

The lieutenant had an Indian girlfriend who lived a short distance from the fort; he visited her each evening. On several occasions Vivia followed him to the girl's home, and on each occasion her bitterness grew.

On a cold winter evening during the end of December 1869, Vivia followed the lieutenant on his trip. This time she hid behind a large rock near a point on the trail where it crossed a small stream. The moon was full and she had a good view of the trail from behind the stone. In the cold, brisk winter air, she could hear the galloping of the lieutenant's horse as he returned to the fort. Just as he crossed the stream, he caught the full charge of Vivia's rifle in the chest and fell hard from his horse to the frozen ground. The next morning his body was found by a passerby and brought to the fort.

A fruitless investigation was held and was finally dropped with the assumption that the lieutenant had been killed by Indians who resented his affection for the Indian maiden.

At first Vivia was happy and relieved; she had achieved the revenge she sought for so many months. But after a few days had passed she became deeply grieved, remorseful, and disturbed over killing the only man she had ever loved. She began leaving her quarters after sundown and going to the lieutenant's grave, where she would weep for hours and pray for forgiveness.

Weak with pneumonia she contracted from long nights of exposure, Vivia apparently collapsed over the grave and froze to death during the night of January 7, 1870.

The romantic story of this brave young girl from Boston and the fact that she was the only female who had served, undetected, in the military deeply touched the commanding officer and other soldiers at the fort. In the center of the national cemetery near the fort a large circle known as the Circle of Honor was set aside for the burial of soldiers who had distinguished themselves as military heroes or outstanding leaders. Among the graves within the Circle of Honor one stone seems out of place. The stone simply reads, "Vivia Thomas, January 7, 1870."

"The Legend of Vivia" by Phillip W. Steele originally appeared in *Ozark Tales and Superstitions*, Pelican Publishing Company, Gretna, Louisiana, 1983, pp. 65-69.

The Cry on Blackbird Hill

Located eight miles north of Decatur (Nebraska) on the Missouri River, Blackbird Hill served the Indians as an observation point. Here, according to legend, the Omaha chief Blackbird was buried sitting upright on his favorite horse. Four years after his death, on August 11, 1804, the hill was visited by the Lewis and Clark expedition. The belief persists that on the night of the October full moon, a woman's scream can be heard at the top of the hill.

ONE FALL IN THE MIDDLE OF the nineteenth century, the Indians discovered a wandering white man who was raving mad and nearly starved. They took him to the medicine man of the tribe. After the Indians had laid the man on a couch in the wigwam, the medicine man sent them away. Then he stroked the white man's forehead and murmured strange words. He selected some dried herbs from his medicine pouch and placed them on the live coals of his fire. Gently he fanned the smoke over the white man.

The man recovered and lived with the Indian for some time. Gradually he began to take an interest in life, and before he left for his home in the East he told the Indian this story.

He said that after he had finished his course in an eastern school, his father had sent him abroad on a business mission. On his way home he was shipwrecked and five years passed before he was able to reach his homeland. In the meantime his mother died; with her last words she asked for her boy. His sweetheart at first waited for him, but finally she yielded to a former suitor. They were married and moved west.

The young man who had been shipwrecked returned. His sister told him what had happened and he set out to find her, hoping that her husband, a boyhood friend of his, would release her. He went westward to California, where people were rushing in search of gold, but his efforts were fruitless. Discouraged, he again started for his home in the east. Sailing down the Missouri River he landed one evening at the foot of Blackbird Hill. A well-marked path led him to a cabin; here, to his great surprise, he found his sweetheart. They each told what had happened in the years since their parting, and the young woman promised to ask her husband to release her and said that she would go with him on the next day.

When the husband returned, the girl told him what had happened. He pleaded with her to stay. He became crazed and struck her with his hunting knife, almost severing her head from her body. Her former sweetheart was near the cabin and saw what was happening. Before he could recover from the shock, the husband had picked the girl up in his arms and had carried her to the edge of the cliff. With a scream he hurled himself and his dead wife into the river below.

The white man then became unconscious and first recovered on the couch in the Indian tipi. He returned to the East, never to be free from the memory of this harrowing experience. The story became known to all Indians. The blood dripping from the girl's body killed the grass on the trail from the cabin to the cliff, and the grass has never since grown on that path. And now, each year, when the October moon is full, that same piercing cry is said to be heard.

"The Cry on Blackbird Hill" originally appeared in *A Treasury of Nebraska Pioneer Folklore*, compiled by Roger L. Welsch, University of Nebraska Press, Lincoln, Nebraska, 1966, pp. 181-182. Reprinted with permission; © 1966 by the University of Nebraska Press.

Fateful Vengeance

Coffin Hollow

ON A POINT OF LAND JUST BELOW my home is a very old cemetery. This cemetery contains the graves of some Civil War soldiers who died during the Jones raid. It is said that one of these soldiers was killed after being captured by the Yanks. This gallant Confederate soldier fought long and hard before being shot in the leg by some unidentified traitor. He was then taken prisoner, loaded on a wagon, and started on his way to prison.

Now a certain Yankee captain had seen his brother shot down by this soldier and hated him for it. He set out in pursuit of the wagon, caught up with it, and like the lowly Yankee dog that he was, placed a bullet through the rebel's head, killing him instantly. The reb was buried in the cemetery previously mentioned and was forgotten.

Some years later, however, the Yankee captain moved to Monongah and began courting a girl from Watson. To get to this girl's house, he had to ride past the cemetery where the soldier was buried. On the first night that he passed the grave, he heard a loud rumble and then that blood-curdling rebel yell. Looking up toward the cemetery, he saw the soldier he had killed, seated atop his coffin, riding it over the hill toward him.

The ex-captain gave a scream, wheeled his horse around, and ran for home. The ghost followed him only as far as the mouth of the hollow, there turning back to his grave. This went on for months on end, until one night some of the captain's friends found him shot through the head with an apparently very old and previously used bullet.

Now these men had heard the captain's story and also knew

183

that the bullet had never been removed from the dead rebel's head. They quickly went to the graveyard and opened the dead man's grave. They found there, to their horror, that the bullet was gone from the reb's head and in his hand was a still-smoking revolver.

From that time on, the wild rebel scream has never again echoed through the hollow, nor has a dead soldier ridden his coffin over the hill. However, to this day, the hollow where this took place is still called Coffin Hollow, and I can still show you the grave of the dead rebel.

"Coffin Hollow" by Ruth Ann Musick originally appeared in *Coffin Hollow and Other Ghost Tales*, University of Kentucky Press, Lexington, Kentucky, 1977, pp. 9-11, © 1977 by the University Press of Kentucky. Reprinted by permission of the publishers.

Phantoms and Spectres

Takaluma, the Phantom Indian

(Floyd Benjamin Streeter recounts the story told to him by the man who met and talked to a ghost late at night, 23 January 1879. Mr. Streeter does not identify this man, but he gives the story in the language of his informant, a cowboy. Reprinted from The Aerend, *IV, Winter, 1933, 157-159.)*

I AM A GRADUATE OF A COLLEGE of the East and am not given to indulgences of absurd fancies, and yet the experience I met with last Thursday night was so remarkable in its character that I am almost inclined to believe it an hallucination, notwithstanding it is still so vividly engraved on the tablets of my memory.

I was engaged in herding cattle by the Saline River in the northern part of Ellis County, Kansas, and on the night mentioned I was belated several miles down the Saline from my camp in Oak Canyon. Not desiring to remain away from camp over night, I urged my jaded horse along up the river until I came to the crossing below Phil Mock's claim, when he suddenly came to a standstill and resisted every effort to induce him to move. Just then the most terrible yell that ever waked the midnight stillness of earth greeted my ears, and looking forward, in the murky gloom I beheld an apparition that chilled the very marrow of my bones. A large powerful-looking Indian—the most perfect speciman of manhood my eyes ever beheld—stood before me. To grasp my revolver and fire at the red man was but the work of an instant; but the result was the most startling shock my nervous system has ever received. The Indian stood erect, unharmed, laughed a low mocking laugh, and then in tones of purest English said: "Does the White Man think his bullet can harm the spirit of Takaluma, the great chief of Inciennes, that has wandered by this beautiful water for more than a thousand years? White Man, I have but little time to talk and I would tell you a tale of wrong and ask you to see that it is redressed."

By this time my fear had merged into a feeling of curiosity and recklessness, and I remarked that if he desired to talk, I would dismount and build a fire. I did so, and the Phantom-Indian, or whatever it was, continued.

"If White Man would be satisfied that I am a spirit from another world, let him feel of this hand my substance."

I did so, and as sure as the whale swallowed Jonah, my hand swept through space. Having thus satisfied myself as to the real phantom character of the form that stood before me, I told him to proceed.

"My people," he continued, "came from the West as many suns ago as the trees of the forest have leaves. They crossed the great water when it was but a little stream between the land of Nod, where dwell the almond-eyed Chinee (heathen Chinee) whose chronology contains an account of the Great Water which destroyed all living things, and of a fertile land beyond. My people in search of this land traveled East for many moons, until coming into this valley. Charmed with its beauty and satisfied with the abundance of game, they built their wigwams and made it their home. Soon, however, a pestilence made its appearance among them, which gathered them all to the happy hunting grounds. Their wigwams decayed and nothing remains to mark the place where once dwelt a mighty people. For years their rest was undisturbed, but at last the white man came, and with his plowshare disturbed the rest of my people."

Just here it occurred to me that he was very familiar with the language, habits, and occupations of the white man, and I compounded a question as to how he obtained all this store of knowledge, to which he replied that association with the spirits of other nations had advised him; his people had spoken the Hebrew language. He continued:

"A few months ago the bones of my father were exhumed and his skull carried away by a resident of this valley. Since then, for an hour each night, I am compelled to wander and search for it, and I ask you to use your influence to have it returned to its resting place. Well know I the party who desecrated my father's grave, but I have not the power to enter habitations. But should the skull not be returned before two more moons shall have waned, then woe to the robbers of the dead, for a spirit will be sent in search of it, with full power to effect an entrance anywhere. My hour is up. I must now return to the mound of my damp sepulchre. Farewell!"

It is to be hoped that the person who carried away the skull of this Indian heeded the warning and returned it so that it is not necessary for spirits to continue their prowling around on cold nights.

"Takaluma, the Phantom Indian" by S.J. Sackett and William E. Koch originally appeared in *Kansas Folklore*, University of Nebraska Press, Lincoln, Nebraska, 1961, pp. 41-42.

The Lady of the Hearth

THE MASSIVE STONE FIREPLACE was the center of family life in pioneer Kentucky. In Lincoln County, in many respects the gateway to the West, a well-to-do family built a new house containing such a chimney, a large hand-hewn stone affair. When the family occupied their new home, they began to notice something odd about the fireplace. It seems that when the fire would die down at night and the embers had been banked for the night, a strange light would appear and shine in the darkness. Investigations revealed that it was not something in or on any of the stones.

The family became terribly frightened as time went on but had not been willing to stay in the room with the light. They employed a man to come and watch the light and attempt to figure out what was causing it. The man became frightened and ran away without getting to the source of the ghostly light.

Two other men were brought in to sit as a pair and study the light when it appeared. That night, the light came forth and soon afterwards the form of a woman materialized on the hearth before their very eyes. They talked with the troubled creature and learned that the fireplace had been over two graves.

The people who owned the house tore away the fireplace and removed the skeletal remains from the graves and buried them nearby in an undisturbed spot. From that time forward the light has not been seen in the big fireplace.

"The Lady of the Hearth" by William Lynwood Montrell originally appeared in *Ghosts Along the Cumberland*, The University of Tennessee Press, Knoxville, Tennessee, 1975, p. 97.

Lady in White

THE KENSEY JOHN HOMESTEAD was one of the busiest and happiest places in the evirons of New Castle, Delaware. But on a cold winter night in the late 1800's, it was the scene of one of the strangest incidents ever to occur within its walls.

It was "visiting day" and several friends of Mrs. John's had come for mid-day dinner. One of the younger couples present had brought their baby with them...all of which was no problem, for Mrs. John owned a much-used cradle. She brought it down from the cooler upstairs bedchamber and placed it by the coal stove in the parlor. The parlor stove on a blustery winter day such as this, kept the coal shuttle busy from the early morning hours on.

It was early afternoon when the snow began to fall. It dropped a fluffy white mantle over all the fields, the barn and the stately manor house. From time to time, a guest would put down her sewing and peer through a lace-curtained window or a husband would knock the ashes out of his pipe bowl as he studied the heightening depths of snow banking against the fence outside.

Finally, Mrs. John announced that dinner was ready, and the company with a murmur of pleasure followed her out of the parlor, across the hall and into the candle-lit dining room, sweet with the fragrance of roasted chicken and bursting hot sweet potatoes.

The young wife lingered behind a moment to tuck the hand-woven blanket tighter around the sleeping form of her baby, then with a final glance at the pine cradle, she left the parlor and joined the others, where one empty high-backed chair awaited her.

It was only shortly after the last of the steaming vegetable bowls had been passed that the young wife paused with her fork in the air. Was that crying from the parlor? She listened tensely. It was. A low murmur of troubled fretting floated across the hallway to her ears. The husband smiled and put a restraining hand on his wife's arm.

"Don't be concerned, dear. She'll quiet down." The wife tried to return the smile and went on eating slowly. The sound grew into a sharp crying, then a fierce wailing. The wife half rose from her chair but the young husband put down his water goblet and faced her with determination. "Let's not start out parenthood designing our every movement around the whims of our child! After all we are dinner guests. Let's act like it!

Mrs. John wiped her lips with a corner of a linen napkin.

"Please, let me look in on the little one. It's no bo—" she started to say.

The young husband nodded acknowledging her courtesy, but assured her that would not be necessary.

As the young mother commenced eating again, slowly and with obvious distress, the piercing screams from the parlor began to subside to a fretting and, finally, diminished to what sounded almost like a cooing of delight.

The wife relaxed and the husband reached out, patting her arm in a congratulatory gesture.

When Mrs. John arose to prepare the final touch of whipped cream on a molasses pudding, the young wife got to her feet abruptly.

"I cannot enjoy a further bite, until I see if our baby is asleep—" With these words she swept past her husband's chair and across the hall into the parlor.

In the darkening afternoon, the only lights in the brown-woodworked room were the flickering oil lamps on the mantel and a dancing light piercing the coal stove's patterned iron-work.

The wife put one hand to her high-necked blue gown and just mangaged to keep herself from calling out. A woman was sitting in a low chair by the baby and with one pale hand was rocking the cradle. She was dressed completely in white, even to a pearl comb in her dark hair and milky-soft kid slippers on her slender feet. As she leaned over the baby's sleeping form, she was softly crooning. The song was somehow, faintly reminiscent of a tune she'd heard as a child herself.

The wife was about to step closer and speak to the woman when her husband swept in through the dorway. "Come, my dear—" he started, then stared at the still-bent-over form at the cradle.

"Who is—"

"I don't know," she said. Then a step forward. "Pardon me, have you just arrived? Truly, we are grateful to you for caring for our baby, but—"

The husband pushed past her and gazed carefully down at the frail form sitting by the cradle. "Not at all necessary," he concluded for his wife. "She is our responsibility, you know, not anyone else's."

The couple stood silently for a moment, waiting for a response. The fragile figure in white silk at their feet, seemed utterly unaware of their presence, only watching with gentle eyes the tiny form before her.

"Come, my dears, you are missing the best pudding this side of the Mason Dixon Line," announced Mrs. John who had breezed in through the parlor door with a rustle of silk skirts.

"Why, goodness gracious! Who is this charming lady?"

The couple turned towards her with a mystified expression. "We were just wondering, if we had retired in such haste to the dining room, we had left behind rather unceremoniously, one of your more genteel and unobtrusive guests," murmured the husband.

"Goodness gracious, no I don't believe I have ever met the young lady, but whoever you be, my dear, you must join us at the table. If you've come to us through that world of snow, you must, indeed, be ready for a goodly roast chicken even if it is a mite less than steaming hot at this point."

Mrs. John rushed forward and with a positive reach of her arm leaned over and pulled the young woman in white to her feet. "Come, you shall sit at the table with us and hurry and catch up so that you may enjoy some of my molasses pudding before there's not a morsel left!"

The pale guest stared as though completely surprised at the interruption, but she followed the forceful direction without a murmur. At the table, from time to time, each guest flicked a studying stare at the delicately-featured woman. None felt it was a good idea to try any conversation with her so she ate in complete silence at her place.

The young mother observed with amazement that the garments of the newly arrived guest were as pure and untouched white as the still falling snow outside the windows. There was something unearthly about her whole demeanor. She longed to share her curiosity about the woman with her husband or the hostess, but there was no opportunity to speak freely.

Nor was there for the remainder of the visit. A visit which extended through the rest of the afternoon, the long dark evening and finally, through the whole night...when it became clear to all, no one would be leaving that house that night. The farm lane was impassable, as would be every road around New Castle.

Mrs. John arose to the occasion with flutter and fortitude.

"We have plenty of accommodations for all," she announced.

"Come, follow me, everybody, and I will show you to your rooms."

"You my dear, seem the most weary and I shall give you the warmest and friendliest room in the house," Mrs. John said with a smile as welcoming as the coal hearth across the room. "Make yourself at home and I shall be up to awaken you at seven for a hearty breakfast!"

She was speaking to the slim, pale-gowned guest who simply followed her into the empty room and turned, closing the bedchamber door behind her without a word.

Mrs. John straightened, obviously a bit piqued for the first time. But with her head held high she started to continue down the hallway with the balance of her guests in tow, when abruptly, she reversed softly, her steps. Tiptoeing back to the first chamber she quietly turned the key in the outside lock of the door and pocketed it in her skirts.

Nobody said a word, but sensing the oddness of the situation, walked down to the far end of the hall at their hostess' suggestion.

Joining them, she whispered, "I assure you that I don't ordinarily lock my guests in their chambers, but there is something about that young woman that is certainly not ordinary. I felt it safer and more reassuring to us all to make certain that she remains in her chamber until I call her in the morning."

Everyone murmured words of agreement, though no one knew how to comment further on the obviously mysterious woman who had arrived into their midst from out of nowhere.

"Let's ask Mrs. John in the morning," suggested the young wife as she tucked her baby into the crook of her arm in the deep feather bed, "If a young woman of that lady in white's description ever came here before or ever lived in this house? Somehow, I think she belongs here. Or did belong here at some time."

But the next morning proved too unnerving to everybody in the house for the wife to ask her questions. When the young couple appeared in the oak dining room for breakfast, only the hired girl was present, pouring thick milk into a tall pitcher.

The couple found Mrs. Kensey John in the parlor, stretched out on a red velour sofa. She was fanning herself, in spite of the cold air in the room.

Suddenly she sat up, completely ruffled. "She's gone," she gasped out. "Gone!"

"You mean, the Lady in White?" asked the young wife.

"None other! She's completely and utterly gone! I locked the door. You saw me! There is no other key. The windows in the room are still bolted on the inside. Yet, she's not to be found anywhere. I tell you, she was not from this earth!"

"But we saw her...touched her. She ate with us," sputtered the young husband.

"I know, but all the same, she was not human! I'm sure of it!"

The rest of the guests assembled around the parlor in quiet consternation. No one could explain the strangest occurrence that probably ever took place in New Castle. As an added note of oddity, the male guests, upon checking, found not a trace of footprints in the snow outside.

Even to this century, though the eerie tale was told and retold in every parlor in the area for years and years, there has never been an answer given.

The farmhouse still stands, well back off the Dupont Highway. I have gazed at its worn walls and hemmed-in fields outlined heavily by modern development.

But, perhaps, nothing will hide the long ago incident of a visit to the John's farmhouse by a ghost gowned in white silk and silence.

"The Lady in White" by Adi-Kent Thomas Jeffrey originally appeared in *More Ghosts in the Valley,* The New Hope Art Shop, New Hope, Pennsylvania, 1973, pp. 71-76.

The Sarah

GHOST SHIPS, IN THE MYTHOLOGY of the sea, are almost as plentiful as barnacles on a rock. One of the most celebrated is the phantom schooner of Harpswell which was seen by many people, usually in the late afternoon, fully rigged and under sail; a breathtaking sight, though apt to vanish without warning in a shimmer of light or a sudden rising of fog. This vision has been immortalized in the poem *The Dead Ship of Harpswell*, by John Greenleaf Whittier, whose opening lines are as follows:

> What flecks the outer gray beyond
> the sundown's golden trail?
> The white flash of a sea-bird's wing,
> or gleam of slanting sail?

The period around 1812 was a splendid time for industrious young men to make a legitimate fortune on the high seas. A couple of boys barely into their twenties could prosper trading cod and lumber for the rum, molasses and coffee of the Indies, which was precisely the career George Leverett and Charles Jose envisioned when they set out from Portland, Maine. Their destination was the Soule Boatyard in South Freeport and their mission was to arrange for the building of their own new vessel. However, shortly after arriving in South Freeport they met the lovely Sarah Soule, fell violently in love with her, and out of sorts with each other. Perhaps because of his Portuguese blood, Jose pursued her more hotly, though in the end it was George Leverett she preferred. After a bitter argument, during which

Charles tried to hurl George into the Royal River, the friendship between the two men ended. Charles disappeared and George proceeded with construction of the ship. When she was finished, he appropriately named her *Sarah* and prepared for his wedding to Sarah Soule.

Ill fortune arose on every side. At first there were strange obstacles in the wedding preparations. Then Captain Leverett found it oddly difficult to line up a crew. Still, he was a determined young man and, at last, with his bride in his house and a crew on his ship, Leverett sailed into Portland harbor to take on cargo for the West Indies. At the same time there arrived a curious black craft which flew no flag and was outfitted with cannon. The ship was the *Don Pedro Salazar* and her captain was none other than Leverett's former partner and romantic rival, Charles Jose.

Much like a storm cloud on the horizon, the *Don Pedro* trailed the *Sarah* south. As the voyage progressed the *Sarah*'s crew grew more and more uneasy and petitioned Captain Leverett to head for Nassau to report the menacing pursuer to the British Admiralty. He never reached the harbor. As soon as the *Don Pedro* saw what course Leverett was taking, she opened fire, killing all but Leverett and severely damaging, though through some miracle, not sinking the unarmed *Sarah*.

Still blinded by jealousy and seeking murderous revenge, Jose could have tortured the survivor in a variety of traditional methods. However, Jose, after looting the ship, chose only to tie Leverett to the foot of the *Sarah*'s mainmast and head him out to sea.

It was then that Leverett experienced an extraordinary phenomenon. Helpless as he was and facing certain death and destruction on an unmanned and shattered vessel, he still was possessed by a strange notion that the ship was under control. Indeed the dead crew began to rise up and take their posts one by one. Sails were set and the ship's course was turned toward home. Captain Leverett, at this point, understandably lost consciousness.

On a bleak November day people on Potts' Point saw a fully rigged yet tragic wreck sailing with uncanny accuracy along the

197

unmarked channel. Suddenly the ship came to a full stop without benefit of an anchor. A pale and silent crew lowered an apparently unconscious man into a boat, rowed him ashore and laid him on a rock, his log book beside him. Without even the squeak of an oar-lock, the ghostly sailors returned to the ship just as a heavy fog suddenly blanketed the harbor. When it had lifted the ship was gone. The unconscious man was soon recognized as George Leverett and it is said that he recovered at least enough to relate this tale, though he surely never went to sea again.

The last sighting of the *Sarah* was in the 1880's on a crystaline summer afternoon. A guest seated on the piazza of Harpswell House looked seaward toward the horizon in time to see a wondrous vision.

A great schooner, under full sail, her canvas gilded in the sun, was heading slowly for the harbor. He summoned a friend, but when they looked again the ship had vanished. Believers say that the magnificient wreck and her ghostly crew, weary from wandering, had reached home port for the last time.

"The Sarah" by Mary Bolte originally appeared in *Haunted New England*, Chatham Press, Old Greenwich, Connecticut, 1972, pp. 37-40. Reprinted by permission of the Chatham Press; © 1972 by Mary Bolte.

The Phantom Bugler

AROUND FOREST GROVE THEY still talk about the Phantom Bugler. He was a huge man, the old bugler. Folks around Forest Grove would see him in the old days, striding through the woods, the bugle slung around his shoulders on a wide leather strap.

His bugle was bigger than an ordinary bugle. The sound it made was different, lower, than the usual music made by a bugle, and those who heard it were apt to confuse it with the sound of the wind in the trees. No one ever heard it, though, unless they were alone in the woods. Then, like a low whisper, it would come to them and, almost like magic, the old bugler would appear on their path.

The old bugler was attacked one day by a cougar. In the course of a terrific fight, he managed to kill the cougar, using his only weapon, the bugle. After the fight, he lay on the path, so weakened by loss of blood that he lapsed into unconsciousness. For two days and two nights he lay in the woods, drifting in and out of consciousness, until he regained enough strength to drag himself back to his tiny cabin.

Since that day, only one man has seen the old bugler and lived to tell about it. He was walking through the woods when he heard a low whistling sound. Thinking it was the wind, he just kept walking. Suddenly, the old bugler appeared, blocking the path. The old man's face was lined with scars, apparently from the fight with the cougar, and he looked mad. He raised the bugle slowly, and then, to the horror of the man from Forest Grove, lunged and swung the bugle at the man's head with force enough to crush his skull. The man ducked and ran, and kept running until he was out of the woods.

This happened nearly 70 years ago, but every few years, some say, someone is found in the woods near Forest Grove with his or her head split open, the wound possibly caused by a blow from an oversized bugle, the work, some say, of the Phantom Bugler.

"The Phantom Bugler" by Mike Helm originally appeared in *Oregon's Ghosts and Monsters*, Rainy Day Press, Eugene, Oregon, 1983, pp. 70-71.

Ghostly Humor

The Great Windham Scare

THE FOLLOWING STORY HAS been variously related, as to details, but with a certain agreement as to the more essential facts. Mr. Larned, in the "History of Windham," places the date of the occurrence in the year 1754, and attributes the scare to the feverish state of the people, under daily expectation of war with the French and Indians. Others fix a later date. We reproduce verbatim the account as printed in Barber's "Historical Collections of Connecticut," which originally appeared in a newspaper with the title prefixed of "Lawyers and Bullfrogs."

"On a dark, cloudy, dismal night in the month of July, A.D. 1754, the inhabitants of Windham, a small town in the eastern part of Connecticut, had retired to rest, and for several hours all were wrapped in profound repose—when suddenly, soon after midnight, the slumbers of the peaceful inhabitants were disturbed by a most terrific noise in the sky, right over their heads, which to many seemed the yells and screeches of infuriated Indians, while others had no way of accounting for the awful sounds, which still kept increasing, but by supposing that the Day of Judgment had certainly come; and to their terrified imaginations, the awful uproar in the upper air seemed the immediate precursor of the clangor of the last trumpet. At intervals, many supposed they could distinguish the calling out of the particular names of Colonels Dyer and Elderkin, two eminent lawyers, and this increased the general terror. But soon there was a rush from every house (the tumult in the air still increasing), old and young, male and female, poured forth into the streets, *in puris naturalibus*, entirely forgetful in their hurry

202

and consternation, of their nether habiliments, and, with eyes upturned, tried to pierce the almost palpable darkness. My venerable informant, who well recollects the event, says that some daring spirits, concluding there was nothing supernatural in the hubbub and uproar overhead, but rather, that they heard the yells of Indians commencing a midnight attack, loaded their guns and sallied forth to meet the invading foe. These valiant heroes on ascending the hill that bounds the village on the east, perceived that the sounds came from that quarter, and not from the skies, as at first believed, but their courage would not permit them to proceed to the daring extremity of advancing eastward, until they had discovered the real cause of alarm, and distress, which pervaded the whole village. Towards morning the sounds in the air seemed to die away.... In the morning, the whole cause of alarm, which produced such distressing apprehensions among the good people of the town, was apparent to all who took the trouble to go to a certain mill-pond, situated about three-fourths of a mile eastward of the village. This pond hereafter, in the annals of fame, forever to be called the Frog Pond, in consequence of a severe drought, which had prevailed many weeks, had become nearly dry, and the Bull Frogs, with which it was densely populated, at the mill, fought a pitched battle on the sides of the ditch which ran through it, for the possession and enjoyment of the fluid which remained. Long and obstinately was the contest maintained: and many thousands of combatants were found defunct, on both sides of the ditch the next morning. It had been uncommonly still, for several hours before the battle commenced, but suddenly, as if by preconcerted agreement, every frog on one side of the ditch, raised the war-cry 'Col. Dyer! Col. Dyer!' and at the same instant, from the opposite side, resounded the adverse shout of 'Elderkin too! Elderkin too!' Owing to some peculiar state of the atmosphere, the awful noises appeared to the distressed Windhamites to be directly over their heads."

The scare subsided, but not so the pleasantry indulged in at the expense of the crestfallen inhabitants of Windham:

Some were well pleased, and some were mad:
  Some turned it off with laughter:
And some would never hear a word
  About the thing thereafter.
Some vowed that if the De'il himself
  Should come, they would not flee him,
And if a frog they ever met,
  Pretended not to see him.

"The Great Windham Scare" by Samuel Adams Drake appeared in *A Book of New England: Legends and Folklore in Prose and Poetry*, Charles E. Tuttle Company, Rutland, Vermont, 1971, pp. 436-438.

Old Joe's Ghost

(As narrated to Eileen Cozine in 1956 by Fred Meyer, then around seventy years old, of Jewell County. The type of unusual animal in the tale is commonly referred to as the "Waumpus" or "Waumpus Cat" and lives in the memory of many people who were reared in the rural areas of this country. The prank of slipping a loaded .22 cartridge in the pipe bowl of an unsuspecting person was standard procedure in the early days. Few, if any, fatalities ever resulted.)

ONE AUTUMN WHEN I WAS A SMALL boy, my parents were building an addition to their little homestead house. The building was being done by a young carpenter, Newt Carey, who lived about two and a half miles away. Each morning he came to work in a farm wagon drawn by a team of horses.

One morning he failed to arrive at the usual hour. When he arrived several hours late he was in a state of high excitement. It happened as he was driving by the home of Joe X that a young girl who was working there came running frantically to the road and begged him to come to the house to help them, for an awful thing had happened.

Now Joe was the neighborhood tippler. While he was an honest hardworking man when sober, he was so addicted to the use of whiskey that it was a rare week in which he was sober more than half of the time. The family consisted of a son David, a lad of about twelve, and several smaller children, the youngest a newborn babe of less than a week. The girl whose terrifying cries attracted Newt's attention was the daughter of a neighbor whose services had been to attend to the household duties until such time as Mrs. X, who was still confined to her bed, would be able to resume her household responsibilities. The day after the arrival of the new baby Old Joe, as he was familiarly known, had suddenly and mysteriously disappeared. No one knew anything of his whereabouts.

Now the "awful thing" to which the girl referred came about in this way. Under the house was a small dark cellar. The only entrance to this part of the residence was through a trap door in the kitchen floor. As the girl was preparing breakfast, she heard a strange noise in the cellar. While somewhat frightened, she managed to gather courage enough to raise the trap door just a bit, and she was shocked to see a great black woolly object which looked to her like the uncombed head of a great giant. She shrieked in fright and immediately closed the trap door and pulled an organ which was standing near by over it. This evidently displeased the apparition, for he immediately set up a loud bellowing sound and proceeded to thump on the trap door and kitchen floor with his head and to thrash about, upsetting boxes and bottles stored in the cellar. It was at this point that the girl ran for help, and seeing Mr. Carey coming down the road, implored his aid. When he arrived, he could hear the strange object still thrashing about in the cellar. He decided it was too much for him to tackle alone since he was unarmed, so he hastily gave the alarm to neighbors, and within an hour several frightened men armed with shotguns, axes, and butcher knives had assembled. By this time the noise had ceased. Some of the bolder, stronger men opened the trap door and, carrying a lantern, went into the cellar. Aside from the fact that the contents of the shelves had been scattered around, there was nothing unusual to be seen or heard. Since Mrs. X and the children were very much afraid, some of the men stayed throughout the day and others came to sit up for the night. Nothing happened until about midnight when in one of the partition walls could be heard a weird scraping, scratching noise. This kept up for several minutes. Then there would be quiet for a while after which similar sounds could be heard in another part of the house. In the weeks that followed there would be several days and nights during which there would be no unusual happenings, and then they could reoccur with renewed vigor. This kept up throughout the winter. The neighbors would sit up until several nights had passed with no demonstration; then they would cease coming.

In the meantime a number of steps were taken to clear up the mystery. The commonly accepted theory was that Old Joe had been murdered and that his ghost was haunting the place. But where was the body? An old abandonded well which had been filled with brush and trash was cleared out, for some were sure that the body was hidden there, but they found nothing. Every ditch, brush patch, and strawstack in the immediate community was carefully searched but of no avail.

Another theory advanced was that Old Joe himself was lurking about and during the night would sneak up to the house and by some means or other cause these strange noises to scare the family and others who might be there. Or perhaps it was some prankster who took delight in scaring people. And if it were a person, they would make it hot for him, whoever he might be, if they ever caught him. To facilitate this they arranged for the village constable or someone deputized by him to be there to arrest the culprit if he were ever apprehended. One night when the regular constable was present, the group of men were passing the time away at a game of pitch. It was customary on occasions such as this for some of the men to bolster up their courage by means of nips from a bottle of whiskey. It was only natural that after a few hours of this that some of them should get to the point when their thinking was a bit confused. On this particular night the constable laid his pipe down on the table for a minute while he shuffled his cards. He picked his pipe up and relighted it, only to have a blast of gunpowder explode in his face. Both frightened and angered, he arose in his might and thundered out, "I arrest you in the name of the law." He then proceeded to nail the warrant which he carried in his pocket to the kitchen door.

To the simple country folk, many of whom were quite superstitious, there was but one explanation of these goings on. The house was haunted. For some unknown reason the ghost or ghouls frequented this house. Old Joe's mysterious departure likely entered in. Would the ghosts confine their activity to this one house, or might they not call on other houses in the community? Housewives shuddered at the thought of staying alone at night, and children dreaded to go outside or into a dark room. Even though the men acted bold and brave, inwardly they felt jittery while walking along a lonely road or by vacant houses at night. At every neighborhood gathering ghosts were the principal topic of conversation, and tales grew in weirdness as they were told over and over again.

As spring approached, the activity of the ghosts became less frequent and finally faded out altogether. Then one warm spring evening Old Joe came trudging down the road toward his home and family. After he took over again there were no more ghosts.

As time wore on, the real plan and procedure gradually came to light. Old Joe had mortgaged his crop to pay debts he had incurred to buy whiskey. Winter was coming on. The family would be without food, fuel, and money to buy other necessities. There was not even any money with which to buy whiskey. With Old Joe around, the neighbors would not likely be very sympathetic. With his being gone and the family in trouble, they would provide for their needs. So Old Joe planned for two things: to mysteriously disappear and to make it appear that the family was in dire trouble. What worse trouble could anyone have than having to live in a haunted house? Old Joe guessed right. All winter long neighbors from far and near brought in meat, flour, eggs, and other foods. The men chopped wood, and if someone noticed that a child needed a new dress or that his shoes were worn out, the word got out and soon their need was supplied. Old Joe had gone to a Nebraska town where he managed to work enough to pay for his board and whiskey. He often chuckled to himself as he read in the newspaper stories which were headlined as ''The Devil Seen Alive,'' ''Peace Officer's Pipe Explodes,'' etc. Credit for the skillful execution of the hoax belongs to the boy David. Just how much of the ghost activity was due to his own imitation and how much was the result of Old Joe's coaching is not known, but the fact remains that the whole thing was carried out with cleverness and precision.

The "awful thing" that appeared in the cellar on that first morning was David himself with the wooly part of an old buffalo robe over his head. He managed to skip out of the cellar and hide the robe while the neighbors were gathering.

The strange noises heard in the walls of the house were made by devices which he manipulated from his bed. The house was a one and a half story building, the upper story of which was not finished. By means of strong cords he would let a device down between the walls of the rooms, and operate it puppet fashion at will. From his sleeping quarters he had access to the walls of every room in the house.

The explosion of the constable's pipe was brought about by his unobtrusively picking up the pipe from the table, and when no one was looking he slipped a loaded cartridge in the refilled pipe.

The events of this story happened a long time ago and I now am an old man. I have never believed in ghosts but even yet as I drive down a country road past a desolate farmhouse, I often feel a cold creepy chill running down my back and find myself recalling that "awful thing" in the dark cellar and the strange noises in the walls of the home of the neighborhood drunk.

"Old Joe's Ghost" by S.J. Sackett and William F. Koch originally appeared in *Kansas Folklore,* University of Nebraska Press, Lincoln, Nebraska, 1961, pp. 46-50.

How the Duyvil Gave
New Amsterdam to the English

NEARLY EVERYTHING IN THE world has two ends, and so has New York City's Manhattan Island. This tale happened at both ends of the island. It started at the southern, lower end and finishes at the northern, upper end.

In the olden, golden days, Manhattan was called New Amsterdam. The Dutch settlers bought the island from the Indians for sixty guilders, which at the time was worth twenty-four dollars, and named it after their famous city in Holland. In the Dutch days the city's population was concentrated at the lower end of the island. Beyond the city were hills and woods with many little villages; on one side of the island was the gleaming Hudson River, on the other side, the sparkling East River.

New Amsterdam was ruled by governors. The mightiest of them all was Peter Stuyvesant, who had a wooden leg and was a great warrior. Next to him in fame was Anthony the Trumpeter. Anthony was big and fat, with long whiskers and a large broad nose that shone like polished copper in a Dutch kitchen. He could hold his breath longer and blow out his breath stronger than an "Dutchman" in New Amsterdam. For that reason Governor Peter Stuyvesant made him the trumpeter of his army and of all the colony. Anthony was very proud of this honor and blew his trumpet all the time.

When he blew the trumpet it was louder than Joshua's trumpet that toppled the walls of Jericho. Whenever the Indians came to battle the Dutch for the wrongs they had committed against them, Anthony would blow his trumpet so loud that it put the Indians to flight.

One day the peg-legged governor heard that the English fleet was coming to attack him and take his city for their British ruler.

The governor called Anthony to his council chamber.

"Anthony," he roared sternly, "cease dallying with your Dutch sweethearts and come to the rescue of your country. The thieving robbers, the English pirates, are coming with their ships to steal the city from our crown. Go out into the villages on the island and villages along the Hudson River and blow your trumpet stronger than you've ever blown it before. Summon all good burghers to come and help defeat the British scoundrels."

"I am going," Anthony replied, "and I'll blow my trumpet loud enough to be heard in the other world. Trust me, Governor Stuyvesant. We'll beat those ruffians so they'll run away like curs with tails between their legs."

Anthony bade farewell to the many Dutch girls with whom he had been friendly and set out, his gilded trumpet hanging on one side of his doublet and his large, heavy stone jug on the other.

It was a windy, stormy day, but Anthony went on valiantly. From time to time he would take a hearty sip from his trusty stone jug and would blow his trusty trumpet. So toward night, he came to the northern end of the island. To get to the other side of the land, he had to cross water. He hallooed for the ferryman, but no ferryman came with any boat. He stormed up and down, he shouted, he even blew his mighty trumpet, but only the blasting wind roared back at him. No ferryman came.

He looked at the choppy waves and took a deep draught from his trusty jug.

"Ha!" he roared, "I'll cross the water *en spuyt den Duyvil* [in spite of the Devil]!" The words were said and the deed was done.

He plunged into the churning cold water, his gleaming trumpet held high in one hand and his trusty jug in the other. With mighty strength of arm and legs he moved forward. But the Duyvil deep down in the Hudson River had heard Anthony's brash boast. Swiftly he came up from the muddy bottom and there he was, looking fiercely at the breasting trumpeter.

The Devil had taken the form of a giant green fish with a huge tail splashing out of the water and raising the waves hill-high. The devil-fish opened his mouth wide enough to swallow ten men in one gulp, and out came a fierce roar. He was steering straight for Anthony.

"Ha, so you think you can spite me! You yoicking, red-nosed minnow, squeaking puny squeaks on your tin trumpet! I'll teach you to dare me!" he bellowed.

He lashed his long tail fiercely in the leaping water.

"I'll show you how to spite me!" he screamed into the wind, and he got hold of Anthony's leg.

The fearless trumpeter brought the trumpet to his lips and let out a blast in the howling gale so fierce that it frightened even the wind. For one moment even the devil-fish let go of Anthony's leg. But he quickly got hold of it again and began pulling the trumpeter down...down...down...deep.

Anthony fought heroically, his fiery nose becoming redder and redder in the dark, stormy night, but he was going down, down...deeper...deeper...Soon there was just a faint gleam of his nose through the black water.

The storm roared wild and the water leaped high, but Anthony wasn't there any more....

That was the reason he did not blow his trumpet that would have roused the Dutch burghers to come to the rescue of fair New Amsterdam. And that was why the English conquered New Amsterdam and called it New York.

But on stormy nights, folks who live on the upper end of Manhattan say they can hear Anthony's blowing trumpet in the roaring winds. For though the Devil conquered Anthony's body, he could never conquer his blowing trumpet. And to this day the place is called "Spuyten Duyvil."

"How the Duyvil Gave New Amsterdam to the English" by M.A. Jagendorf originally appeared in *The Ghost of Peg-leg Peter and Other Stories of Old New York*, The Vangaurd Press, New York, New York, 1965, pp. 31-36.

Index